NORTH AMERICAN GUIDE

TO NUDE RECREATION

The American Association For Nude Recreation
1703 North Main Street
Kissimmee, Florida 34744-3396
800/879-6833
Web Site: http://www.aanr.com

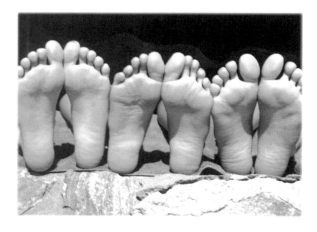

ACKNOWLEDGMENTS

EXECUTIVE EDITOR
Roslyn Scheer

PROJECT EDITOR
Julie Bagby

DESIGN
Michael Gill

LAYOUT/DESIGN
Angelique Priore

EDITORIAL WRITERS
Jill Gross
John Sikes
Pete Williams
Richard T. Turner

ASSISTANTS TO THE EDITOR
Kathleen Bokun
Eva Bratton

COVER PHOTOS
By Robb Maag
Courtesy Bare Necessities

CONTENTS

A NUDE BEGINN

A NUDE BEGINN

Free yourself.
Love your body.

Slip on a tee-shirt, wrap a fluffy towel around yourself or, better yet, simply wear nothing at all.

Indulge in the total body comfort of nude recreation. Soak in the glorious sensation of sun on your bare skin. Feel your muscles relax as your entire body begins to unwind.

Nude recreation is a wonderful way to pamper yourself. It's a natural choice for relieving stress, and leaving your everyday cares behind. Whether reading, working out, or listening to music, everything feels more comfortable without the restriction of clothes. Imagine being able to hike, bike, swim, play volleyball, socialize, and relax in the hot tub, all without ever having to decide what to wear.

NG

"All of these parks are places where social nudity can be relished in dignity, peace, and privacy."

Nude recreation. For some of us it's an adventure waiting to happen. A chance to try out skinny-dipping for the first time. For others it's a way of life. The way we would like to spend the majority of our day. If you are a lifelong nudist, or a first time visitor, AANR's *North American Guide to Nude Recreation* was created for you. Look through the guide, and find out the secret of how to pack less and relax more.

NORTH AMERICAN GUIDE TO NUDE RECREATION

Paging through the *North American Guide to Nude Recreation* is a mini vacation in itself. The guide is packed with stunning color photos of resorts from Northwest Canada all the way to the Caribbean.

Meander your way about the guide. You'll visit everything from rolling wooded terrain and secluded campsites to mountain vistas and glamorous resorts. Many of AANR's clubs and resorts are located in beautiful, natural settings where nude recreation can be enjoyed in dignity, peace and privacy. Other clubs combine their spectacular surroundings with the utmost in quality accommodations. Whatever your choice of lodging, or your budget—from rustic cabins to extraordinary villas—there's a vacation spot just right for you.

The *North American Guide to Nude Recreation* also contains a listing of nonlanded, travel clubs. These clubs are social groups that don't own or

lease grounds. Members hold events at private homes and often travel together to landed clubs or other nude recreation getaways.

The *North American Guide to Nude Recreation* is the most extensive listing available of nude recreational clubs and parks in North America. Inside the guide you'll find easy to follow maps and club phone numbers. Consider this guide your passport for locating the perfect nude recreation experience.

WHO YOU WILL MEET
WHO YOU WILL MEET

When you arrive at an AANR club or park

you'll meet members of all ages. You'll see singles, couples, and children looking a lot like tiny cherubs. People look their best when they're not wearing anything at all. That's because nudity flatters every skin tone.

Nude recreation is enjoyed by many different people. Some visitors will be quiet, while others are ready for lively conversation. Some will be retired, and others will work right in the local community. You'll meet dentists, truck drivers, postal carriers, salespeople, business owners, engineers, musicians, and stay-at-home parents. And you might not be able to tell the difference.

"Consider this guide your passport for locating the perfect nude recreation experience."

Without clothes to tell you about someone, you'll find yourself slowing down a bit—and then wanting to take the time to learn about someone's true inner personality. Somehow being nude allows us to communicate more honestly and openly. Eye contact comes naturally, listening becomes a pleasure, and friendships are formed quite easily.

As you meet and talk with first time visitors or long-time club members, conversation often drifts to how everyone first enjoyed nude recreation. Each visitor has their own story. It's a common thread that weaves together all the AANR clubs and parks. You may want to add your story to the fabric of AANR.

There's a wide mix of visitors at all the AANR clubs and resorts. In fact many visitors say that each club, as well, has a personality all its own. Whether famous for their volleyball tournaments, outstanding facilities, or the art of turning a potluck dinner into a gourmet feast, each club has a comfortable style that suits it perfectly. All the clubs are individually owned and operated, which maintains that one-of-a-kind quality. As you visit the many AANR clubs, resorts, and parks, you'll find more than one is a perfect fit for you.

BODY ACCEPTANCE

BODY ACCEPTANCE

Nude recreation is one of the healthiest trends of our times. Nude recreation allows us to accept ourselves for who we are and to feel comfortable about our bodies. Experiencing who you are inside is more important than what you show on the outside.

Look around at any AANR club or resort. Just like anywhere else, you'll find a full range of shapes and sizes. It doesn't matter if you're at a quaint bed and breakfast or a huge ultra modern resort, you'll see physiques that are short, tall, thin, full figured, and muscular.

Some visitors will have golden tans. Others will use lots of sun screen. Many will carry visual reminders of past surgeries. Your outward appearance is really of no concern. Free yourself to enjoy nude recreation.

RESORTS
ARE
FAMILY
FRIENDLY

There is no better recommendation for nude recreation than the high spirits of the children of AANR clubs and resorts. They joyfully play, run and splash, all without a care—or a stitch of clothes.

Watch the children romp with a glorious zeal for life. No more sandy bottoms to hold them down. And the best part of it all? A bath is just a hop, skip and a jump into the nearest lake. Nudity is natural.

Nude recreation recaptures that small inner child. Let yourself remember. Build a sand castle. Lounge on an inner tube. Or rest in the shade. Then close your eyes and let the wind softly caress your skin. These are the delightful, simple pleasures, that visitors of all ages can enjoy.

MIND & BODY WELLNESS

MIND & BODY WELLNESS

Picture yourself relaxing on the beach. Your body is completely free. Your chaise lounge is pointed towards the sun. A cool drink is at your side, and your favorite book is in your lap. Feel the total body comfort of sunbathing in the nude. That is pure mind and body wellness.

Talk with any member at an AANR club, and they'll say that as they remove their clothes, they remove their daily stress as well. You can tap into this stress-reduction plan. Spend some time in the sun. Let your skin soak in the healing warmth. The experience is awesome. The release of stress is powerful.

If the weather is a bit chilly, steep yourself in the nearest hot tub. Feel the water surround every curve, cradling your body. Lay back, relax, talk, or let your mind lazily wander.

Later you can visit the clubhouse. Or walk around the grounds. Everything is so easy. You don't have to worry about what to wear, if you brought along the right accessories. All you need is a comfortable pair of shoes and a towel. Imagine the time you'll save. No more worries. Decide where to go, and you're off.

Without the restriction of clothes, we give ourselves freedom. A chance to grow to our full potential. With renewed confidence we're able to try new things. Perhaps a rousing game of water volleyball, a quick try at ping pong, or even horseback riding. Spending time at an AANR club is healthy fun for men, women and families. Enjoy nude recreation for both your physical and mental well-being. It will awaken your spirit and soothe your soul.

WHAT IS AANR?

The American Association for Nude Recreation (AANR) has 50,000 members and 225 clubs that span the North American continent. It's the oldest, largest and most respected nudist organization in North America.

We welcome you to join AANR at any time. As a member you'll receive many member benefits. Every time you visit an AANR club you'll receive a 20 percent discount on gate fees.

In addition, every member of AANR receives *The Bulletin*, a professionally produced 48 page monthly newspaper. *The Bulletin* has photos and articles to keep you current on the entire world of nude recreation. There are also articles on AANR members, places to visit, and information about clubs all over North America. Special features are written about exciting new nude recreational opportunities such as nude cruises, or remote Caribbean getaways.

"Without the restriction of clothes, we give ourselves freedom."

AANR was originally called The American Sunbathing Association (ASA). It was founded in 1931 by the diligent efforts of a flamboyant minister named Ilsley Boone. Through his organizational skills and flair for public relations, Boone set the stage for rapid expansion of nudism in the United States. In 1995 the ASA changed its name to the American Association for Nude Recreation (AANR). Through the years AANR has continued to advocate the rights of nudists to associate freely in a peaceful, wholesome manner. The battle to safeguard this right is still one of the most important issues the association faces today.

As a member of AANR you'll have the satisfaction of belonging to a strong organization that supports and promotes nude recreation in the United States and Canada through its governmental and public affairs departments.

For more information about joining the American Association for Nude Recreation contact the AANR office at: 1703 North Main Street, Kissimmee, Florida 34744-3396. Or call the office at: 800/TRY-NUDE. You can also visit the AANR web site at: http://www.aanr.com. The American Association for Nude Recreation welcomes you to visit one of its clubs, parks or resorts, soon!

STATE	RV SITES	RENTAL TRAILERS	RENTAL UNITS	CONVENIENCE STORE	LAUNDROMAT	SNACK BAR	RESTAURANT	SWIMMING POOL	WHIRLPOOL/SPA	SAUNA	TENNIS	VOLLEYBALL	SHUFFLEBOARD	PLAYGROUND	EXERCISE EQUIPMENT	RECREATION HALL	CLUB NAME
● ALABAMA	■		■					■			■		■			■	Gymno-Vita Park
● ARIZONA	■							■	■		■						Arizona Hidden Valley Retreat
	■		■					■	■		■	■		■		■	Jardin del Sol
	■		■		■		■	■	■	■	■	■	■	■	■	■	Shangri-la II
● CALIFORNIA				■				■	■	■	■	■		■		■	Elysium Fields
			■	■			■	■	■	■	■	■			■	■	Desert Shadows Inn
	■	■		■	■		■	■	■		■	■	■	■		■	Glen Eden Sun Club
	■	■	■		■		■	■	■	■	■	■	■	■	■	■	Laguna del Sol
	■		■	■		■	■	■	■	■	■	■	■	■	■	■	Lupin Naturist Club
	■							■			■	■	■	■		■	McConville
	■		■				■	■	■	■	■	■	■	■		■	Olive Dell Ranch
	■		■	■		■	■	■	■	■	■	■	■				Buff Creek Nudist Resort
	■							■	■			■	■	■		■	Sequoians Family Nudist Park
	■	■	■			■			■				■	■			Silver Valley Sun Club
	■		■		■	■		■	■	■	■			■		■	Swallows
			■					■	■								The Terra Cotta Inn
● COLORADO	■	■	■				■	■	■	■	■	■	■			■	Mountain Air Ranch
● CONNECTICUT	■		■		■	■		■	■	■	■	■	■		■	■	Solair Recreation League
	■	■		■	■	■		■			■	■		■		■	Sunridge Resort
● FLORIDA	■		■	■				■	■	■	■	■	■	■	■		Club Paradise at Paradise Lakes
	■		■					■	■		■	■	■	■		■	Cypress Cove
	■	■	■		■			■	■		■	■	■	■		■	Gulf Coast Resort
			■					■	■	■	■	■	■	■	■	■	The Island Group
	■	■	■			■	■	■	■		■	■	■	■		■	Lake Como Club
	■	■			■	■		■	■			■				■	Riviera Naturist Resort
	■	■	■		■			■	■		■	■	■	■	■	■	Seminole Health Club
	■		■		■			■	■		■	■	■			■	Sunburst Resort
	■	■	■					■	■			■	■	■			Sunnier Palms
	■		■		■	■		■	■			■	■			■	Sunny Sands Resort
	■	■			■	■	■	■	■	■	■		■	■		■	Sunsport Gardens
● GEORGIA			■	■	■	■		■	■					■	■	■	Bell Acres
	■		■	■	■	■	■	■	■		■	■	■	■		■	Hidden Valley
	■		■		■	■		■	■			■	■	■	■	■	Mountain Creek Grove
	■	■	■	■			■	■	■	■		■		■	■	■	Serendipity Park
● IDAHO	■							■			■		■				Bare Backers
● ILLINOIS	■		■				■		■		■	■				■	Blue Lake Club
● INDIANA	■	■	■				■	■	■	■	■	■	■			■	Fern Hills Club
	■		■					■	■	■	■	■	■			■	Lake O'The Woods Club
	■		■	■		■		■	■	■	■	■	■			■	Sunny Haven
	■	■	■					■	■				■	■		■	Sunshower Country Club
	■	■	■	■		■		■					■	■		■	Tri-State Country Club
● KANSAS	■	■						■	■		■	■	■	■		■	Prairie Haven
	■		■			■		■	■			■	■	■	■		Sandy Lane Club
● LOUISIANA	■	■			■	■	■	■	■			■	■	■	■	■	La Pines Ranch

STATE	RV SITES	RENTAL TRAILERS	RENTAL UNITS	CONVENIENCE STORE	LAUNDROMAT	SNACK BAR	RESTAURANT	SWIMMING POOL	WHIRLPOOL/SPA	SAUNA	TENNIS	VOLLEYBALL	SHUFFLEBOARD	PLAYGROUND	EXERCISE EQUIPMENT	RECREATION HALL	CLUB NAME
MARYLAND	■		■				■				■	■	■			■	Maryland Health Society
	■		■	■	■		■	■	■	■	■	■	■			■	Pine Tree Associates
MASSACHUSETTS	■	■	■					■	■	■	■					■	Sandy Terraces
	■	■	■			■	■	■	■	■	■	■	■	■	■	■	Berkshire Vista Resort
MICHIGAN	■		■	■	■	■		■			■	■	■			■	Forest Hills
	■		■				■	■	■	■	■	■	■	■	■	■	Sunshine Gardens Resort
	■	■			■		■	■	■	■	■	■	■	■		■	Whispering Oaks
	■		■	■			■	■	■		■	■	■			■	Turtle Lake Resort
MINNESOTA	■	■			■		■	■	■	■	■		■			■	Avatan
	■	■					■			■	■	■	■			■	Oakwood Club
MISSOURI	■		■	■	■			■		■	■	■	■			■	Forty Acre Club
NEVADA	■	■	■	■	■			■	■	■			■				Las Vegas Sun Club
NEW JERSEY			■		■			■	■	■	■		■			■	Rock Lodge Club
NEW YORK	■	■		■		■		■			■		■	■		■	Buckridge
	■	■	■			■	■	■	■		■	■	■			■	Empire Haven
	■							■		■	■		■			■	Full-Tan Sun Club
	■							■			■						Hudson Valley Naturally
NORTH CAROLINA	■	■	■			■		■	■	■	■					■	Bar-S-Ranch
	■		■					■	■		■					■	Nirvana Sun Resort
	■	■						■	■	■	■	■	■			■	Whispering Pines
OHIO	■	■				■					■		■			■	Alpine Resort
	■			■	■	■					■		■			■	Cedar Trails
	■	■	■	■				■	■		■	■	■			■	Green Valley
	■		■		■			■	■	■	■	■	■		■	■	Paradise Gardens
OKLAHOMA	■							■	■		■	■	■		■	■	Oaklake Trails
	■							■	■	■	■	■	■	■		■	Sun Meadow
OREGON	■				■	■		■	■		■	■				■	Restful Haven
	■	■	■	■				■	■		■	■				■	Squaw Mountain Ranch
	■	■	■		■	■		■	■	■	■	■	■			■	The Willamettans
PENNSYLVANIA	■		■			■	■	■	■	■	■		■	■		■	Beechwood Lodge
	■	■									■					■	Broken Arrow
	■	■					■				■		■			■	Pen-Mar Club (PA/MD border)
	■		■				■	■	■	■	■	■	■			■	Penn Sylvan Health Society
	■		■		■	■		■	■	■	■	■	■	■	■	■	White Thorn Lodge
RHODE ISLAND	■		■			■		■	■		■		■			■	Dyer Woods
SOUTH CAROLINA	■	■	■	■				■	■		■			■	■	■	Carolina Foothills
			■	■	■	■	■	■			■			■		■	Cedar Creek
	■	■	■		■	■		■			■	■	■			■	Sunair Health Park
TENNESSEE	■	■	■	■		■		■			■	■	■			■	Rock Haven Lodge
	■	■	■	■	■	■		■			■	■	■	■	■	■	Timberline Lodge Resort
TEXAS	■	■					■	■	■	■	■	■	■			■	Bluebonnet
	■	■	■	■	■		■	■	■		■	■	■			■	Live Oak Nudist Resort
	■	■						■	■		■	■	■			■	Natural Horisun
	■		■			■		■	■		■	■	■	■		■	Riverside Ranch

FACILITY OVERVIEW STATE	RV SITES	RENTAL TRAILERS	RENTAL UNITS	CONVENIENCE STORE	LAUNDROMAT	SNACK BAR	RESTAURANT	SWIMMING POOL	WHIRLPOOL/SPA	SAUNA	TENNIS	VOLLEYBALL	SHUFFLEBOARD	PLAYGROUND	EXERCISE EQUIPMENT	RECREATION HALL	CLUB NAME
● TEXAS (continued)	■		■	■	■		■	■	■		■	■	■	■		■	Sahnoans
	■	■		■	■	■	■	■		■	■	■	■	■	■	■	Sandpipers Holiday Park
	■	■	■			■	■	■	■	■		■	■			■	Sunny Pines
	■	■	■			■		■	■		■	■	■	■	■	■	Vista Grande Ranch
● VERMONT	■	■	■	■							■	■	■			■	Forest City Lodge
● VIRGINIA	■		■		■	■		■	■	■		■	■	■		■	White Tail Park
● WASHINGTON	■	■	■	■				■	■	■		■	■	■		■	Fraternity Snoqualmie
	■		■		■		■	■	■	■		■	■	■		■	Kaniksu Ranch
	■							■			■			■			Lake Associates Recreation Club
	■	■	■	■	■		■		■	■	■	■	■	■		■	Lake Bronson Club
● WEST VIRGINIA	■		■	■			■	■	■		■	■		■	■	■	Avalon
● WISCONSIN	■	■	■	■		■		■				■		■	■	■	Valley View Recreation Club
● CANADA/ALBERTA	■						■	■	■			■					Helios Nudist Association
● ALBERTA	■				■			■				■				■	Sunny Chinooks Association
● BRITISH COLUMBIA	■		■		■		■	■	■	■		■	■	■		■	Sunny Trails Club
● MANITOBA	■	■	■				■	■	■		■	■	■			■	Crocus Grove Sun Club
	■	■					■				■					■	Musqua Meadows
● ONTARIO	■	■	■			■	■	■	■	■	■	■	■	■		■	Ponderosa Nature Resort
● SASKATCHEWAN	■	■				■		■		■	■	■	■	■	■	■	Green Haven Sun Club

GYMNO-VITA PARK

P.O. Box 121
Vandiver, AL 35176

ALABAMA

205/672-7105

ACCOMMODATIONS & RECREATION

RV Sites
Rental Rooms
Swimming Pool
Volleyball
Receation Hall
Playground

Club Personality
Gymno-Vita Park, a club in the southern tradition, is a safe, serene and friendly place where families with children, and couples only, are welcome. Among its other courtesies, the park offers nature lectures for guests interested in learning about local flora and fauna.

Description of Grounds
A carefully planned collection of buildings and recreational facilities in the center of 110 acres of natural forest, Gymno-Vita's amenities include a lawn area, a small lake, and one-half mile of fish-filled creek.

ARIZONA

520/568-4027

ARIZONA HIDDEN VALLEY RETREAT

55551 W. La Barranca
Maricopa, AZ 85239

General Information
Open year-round, Arizona Hidden Valley Retreat is a landed club with 60-plus acres in the pristine Arizona desert. Residents, members and guests enjoy the pool, two spas, ramada, clubhouse, bathhouse and lawn. Enjoy soaking up the sun under crystal clear skies, strolling around the grounds, or hiking on the adjacent BLM wilderness area. RV hookups are in place, with more to come. Restaurants, casino, and stores are 7 miles from the grounds. Fly into the on-grounds airstrip. Snowbirds are welcome.

ACTIVITIES & RECREATION

Swimming Pool, Two Spas
Water and Sand Volleyball
Camping, Tent and RV Sites
Desert Hikes
Mountain Biking
Sunbathing

Special Events
Visits from Other Clubs
Seminars
Holiday Cookouts
Stargazing

ARIZONA WILDFLOWERS

ARIZONA

P.O. Box 26465
Phoenix, AZ 85068

ACTIVITIES & RECREATION

Pool Parties and Potlucks
Campouts and Boat Trips
Children's Activities
Holiday Parties
Special Events

General Information
Guests who value the high standards of family nudism are welcome—whether single or married, young or old. Arizona Wildflowers—a nonlanded group—places a premium on respect for friends, and on maintaining the compatibility of the group. Please write for additional information.

ARIZONA
520/293-5854

BUFF-A-TEERS

5775 North First Avenue
Tucson, AZ 85718

ACTIVITIES & RECREATION

General Information
The Buff-A-Teers are families and singles who love the sun, the nudist lifestyle and the benefits of healthful living. Members meet weekly for fellowship and dining excursions to restaurants in Tucson and the surrounding area. Special holiday celebrations and potluck dinners are held at members' homes and local clubs.
Fax: 520-293-6712
E-mail: merritte@aol.com

Special Events
Annual Nude New Year's Extravaganza
Call for Information on Other Special Events

Dining Get-Togethers at Local Restaurants
Travel to Arizona and California Landed Clubs

CANYON WATERWAY ADVENTURES

P.O. Box 36893
Tucson, AZ 85740-6893

ARIZONA
520/682-7217

ACTIVITIES & RECREATION

Houseboat cruising and scouting adventures. Hiking and exploring Indian ruins. Water sports, fishing, floating, swimming, sunbathing. Spectacular sunrises and sunsets offer fantastic photography opportunities.

General Information
Canyon Waterway Adventures offers a unique experience for members of all ages. An adventure back in time, exploring the twists 'n turns of Arizona and Utah's spectacular Lake Powell. Pure relaxation mixed with a touch of high adventure aboard a custom 54-foot houseboat.

ACTIVITIES & RECREATION

"A million miles from Monday . . ."

Club Personality
At El Dorado Hot Spring, where common areas are free of tobacco, alcohol, and pets, an eclectic group of natural hot mineral water lovers welcomes responsible visitors. Call for summer hours, June to September.

Description of Grounds
A rustic—but developing—hot spring situated on 7 flat desert acres with mountain views on three sides. Amenities include tent and RV camping, electricity, water, and dump station. Nudity in enclosed spring areas only, at this time. Newcomers can experience the easy transition to freedom from bathing suits in separate private pool areas. The spring is within 1/2 mile of all essential services.
Web site:
http://www.el-dorado.com/hotwater/
E-mail: hotspring@el-dorado.com

Neighboring Sights and Attractions
Within reasonable driving distance are the Quartzsite winter mecca, petroglyphs, hiking, rock hounding, Grand Canyon, Phoenix World Zoo, International Raceway, mountain biking, four wheeling, and Mexican shopping.

Honored Discounts
Discounts for AANR, INF, TNS, NLI and CSN members.

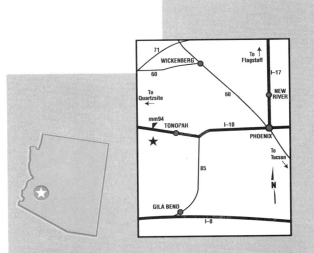

Directions
From Phoenix travel 40 miles west on I-10. Take Exit 94, and go south over the highway. Take a right at the filling station on Indian School Road. Go west 0.1 miles; club is on the south (left) side of the road at 41225 West Indian School Road.

FACILITIES

ACCOMMODATIONS

- Wheelchair Access
- Vacation Villas
- ■ Cabins (2)
- ■ Rooms (2)
- Cable TV
- In-room Telephone
- Trailers
  - heated
  - w/bath
  - cooking
- Restaurant
- Lounge
- Snack Bar
- Store

CAMPING

- ■ Tent Spaces
- ■ R/V Spaces (20)
  - ● w/elec (16)
  - ● w/water (16)
  - w/sewer
- ■ Disposal Station
- ■ Showers
  - ● cold (1)
  - ● hot (3)
- Laundromat
- ■ Community Kitchen
- ■ Picnic Tables (8)
- ■ Playground ("A" frame swing)
- ■ Pets/Leash only

RECREATION

- ■ Swimming Pool (18' x 40')
- Lake
- ■ Whirlpool/Spa
- Sauna
- Exercise Equipment
- ■ Tennis
- ■ Volleyball
- Shuffleboard
- ■ Horseshoes
- Pentanque
- Miniten
- Badminton
- Fishing
- ■ Recreation Hall
- Children's Activities
- Teen Activities
- ■ Hiking Trails, Boot Hill, Chapel

● denotes availability
■

INFORMATION

Club Personality
A jewel in a desert setting, Jardin del Sol is a user-friendly, family oriented nudist park catering to folks who enjoy nature, ecology, astronomy, hiking, sports and fellowship. A club that stresses stresslessness.

Description of Grounds
Encompassing more than 40 acres, Jardin del Sol is an oasis in the Sonoran Desert. Its sparkling pool reflects the majestic saguaro cacti, palo verde, mesquite, cat claw and ironwood trees. The grounds have been left nearly as they were found, with unobtrusive facilities and meandering trails. Nearby mountains are a haven for desert wildlife.

Neighboring Sights and Attractions
Arizona Sonoran Desert Museum, missions, Mt. Lemmon Recreational Area, Pima Air Museum, Biosphere II, Mexico, Tombstone, and more.

Honored Discounts
10 to 40 percent discounts on daily grounds fees for current card-carrying members of national nudist organizations.

Directions
At the club's request, map and directions are not provided. To receive directions, please write to the club.

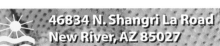

SHANGRI LA II

46834 N. Shangri La Road
New River, AZ 85027

ARIZONA
602/465-5959

FACILITIES

ACCOMMODATIONS

- ■ Wheelchair Access
- ■ Vacation Villas
- ■ Cabins
- ■ Rooms
  - Cable TV
  - In-room Telephone
  - Trailers
    - heated
    - w/bath
    - cooking
- ■ Restaurant
  - Lounge
  - Snack Bar
  - Store

CAMPING

- ■ Tent Spaces
- ■ R/V Spaces
  - ● w/elec
  - ● w/water
  - ● w/sewer
- ■ Disposal Station
- ■ Showers
  - ● cold
  - ● hot
- ■ Laundromat
  - Community Kitchen
- ■ Picnic Tables
- ■ Playground
- ■ Pets/Leash only

RECREATION

- ■ Swimming Pool (1200 sq.ft.)
  - Lake
- ■ Whirlpool/Spa
- ■ Sauna
- ■ Exercise Equipment
- ■ Tennis
- ■ Volleyball
- ■ Shuffleboard
- ■ Horseshoes
  - Pentanque
  - Miniten
  - Badminton
  - Fishing
- ■ Recreation Hall
- ■ Children's Activities
- ■ Teen Activities
- ■ Other (Bocce Ball Court)

INFORMATION

Club Personality

A private, family oriented, clothing-optional nudist resort with friendly members always ready to welcome new arrivals. At Shangri La the warm spirit of the membership is rivaled only by the warm rays of the desert sun.
Fax: 602/465-5900
Web site: http://home.sprynet.com/sprynet/sl2/sl2.htm
E-mail: sl2@sprynet.com

Description of Grounds

A true Shangri La— 38 acres of pristine desert landscape nestled within the foothills of Arizona's Black Canyon, yet only 45 minutes from the Phoenix Sky Harbor International Airport.

Neighboring Sights and Attractions

The Grand Canyon, Old Tucson, Sedona, Oak Creek Canyon, and Nogales, New Mexico, with its unique shopping, are all an easy drive from Shangri La II Resort.

Honored Discounts

10 percent discount on daily grounds fees and RV spaces for AANR and affiliated members.

Directions

From the South: I-17 to Exit 223 (Carefree Highway), near the northern Phoenix city limits. East 4 miles to 7th STREET, not Ave. North 6.9 miles to Shangri-La Road. West to the entrance.

From the North: I-17 Exit 232 turn left (East) under Freeway to East Frontage Road, turn left (North) 0.5 miles to New River Road, turn right (East) 5.5 miles to Shangri-La Road, turn right (West) to entrance.

CALIFORNIA

P.O. Box 1053
Gardena, CA 90249

AIR-A-TANS

General Information

Air-A-Tans is a family oriented travel group drawing members from the greater Los Angeles area. Founded in 1948, it is the oldest nudist travel club in AANR. Members visit different camps and resorts that offer a wide range of facilities. Couple, family and single memberships are available, with inquiries welcome from folks seriously interested in learning about nude recreation.

ACTIVITIES & RECREATION

Visits to Landed Clubs
Socials
Potlucks
Holiday Parties
Camping Events
In-Town Meetings

CANYON SUN CLUB

CALIFORNIA

P.O. Box 5053
San Bernardino, CA 92412

ACTIVITIES & RECREATION

Travel to Landed Clubs

General Information

A nonlanded club providing members with an AANR membership card—the passport to visiting landed clubs.

INFORMATION

Club Personality

The original clothing-optional day resort featuring a friendly, diverse membership and Elysium Institute's educational workshops and classes in personal growth, interpersonal relationships, stress release and the essential wholesomeness of the human body. Massage, tai chi, karate, yoga, aqua-robics, Native American teachings, tennis, social dinners and more.

Description of Grounds

Lush, safe, and secluded eight-acre oasis nestled in the beautiful Santa Monica Mountains, only 30 minutes from Los Angeles. Hilltop hydro pool, heated swimming pool, sauna, tennis court, volleyball courts, community rooms, kitchen, and luxuriously landscaped lawns. Limited overnight available.

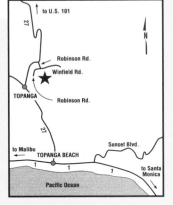

Neighboring Sights and Attractions

28 miles from LAX. Less than one hour from Universal Studios, Six Flags Magic Mountain, Hollywood, Malibu, Santa Monica beaches, and Rodeo Drive in Beverly Hills. Surrounded by the 250,000 acre Santa Monica State Wilderness and Recreation Area.

Honored Discounts

Discounts for INF, AANR, and The Naturist Society members. Call for discount rates.

Directions

Highway 101 to Topanga South exit. South on Topanga Boulevard up the hill 7.5 miles. Just after passing 1105 Topanga, to the right, look for the Elysium Fields sign at Robinson Road. Turn off to the left and follow the signs that lead to the front gate of Elysium Fields.

Elysium Fields

DESERT SHADOWS INN

1533 Chaparral Road
Palm Springs, CA 92262

CALIFORNIA
800/292-9298

FACILITIES

ACCOMMODATIONS

- Wheelchair Access
- Vacation Villas (36)
  Cabins
- Rooms (34)
- Cable TV
- In-room Telephone
  Trailers
    heated
    w/bath
    cooking
- Restaurant
- Lounge
  Snack Bar
- Store

CAMPING

- Tent Spaces
  R/V Spaces
    w/elec
    w/water
    w/sewer
  Disposal Station
  Showers
    cold
    hot
  Laundromat
  Community Kitchen
  Picnic Tables
  Playground
  Pets/Leash only

RECREATION

- Swimming Pool (3)
  Lake
- Whirlpool/Spa (2)
- Sauna
- Fitness Center
- Tennis
- Volleyball
  Shuffleboard
  Horseshoes
  Pentanque
- Badminton
  Fishing
- Recreation Hall, Dances
  Children's Activities
  Teen Activities
- Putting Green
- Tranquil Lagoon and
  Exotic Waterfall

• denotes availability

INFORMATION

Club Personality
Palm Springs' only world class resort and condominium vacation. An enchanting oasis where summer never ends. Combines the romantic charm of a secluded inn with all the luxuries of a full-service resort and spa facility complete with three pools.
Local: 760/325-6410   Fax: 760/327-7500
Web site: http://www.cybernude.com/dshadows
E-mail: 76142.2071@compuserve.com

Description of Grounds
Three unique vacations on one magnificent property: The Courtyard features rooms with designer decorated suites, "quiet pool" and misting system. Full Spa Services; The Chaparral hosts a full-service restaurant, bar, lighted tennis court, putting green, water volleyball and two outdoor spas; Deluxe condominiums feature one and two bedrooms with private balcony, jacuzzi tubs and fireplaces.

Directions
From 10 east bound: Exit Highway 111/Palm Springs exit. Take Highway 111 (Palm Canyon Drive) 9 miles to Vista Chino (third stop light). Turn left. Go two blocks to Chaparral Road—one block past Indian Canyon—and turn right.

From 10 west bound: Exit Date Palm/Vista Chino exit. Turn left at stop sign and go over overpass to Vista Chino. Turn right. Two blocks past Avenida Caballeros is Chaparral Road. Turn left on Chaparral Road.

"An enchanting **oasis** where **summer** never ends."

Neighboring Sights and Attractions
Palm Springs Aerial Tram, three casinos, Fabulous Follies, ancient Indian canyons, International Film Festival, 84 golf courses and exceptional shopping. Day trips to Disneyland, Universal Studios, Hollywood, San Diego Zoo, Black's Beach and Sea World.

Honored Discounts
Discounts to AANR, TNS, INF and CCBN members.

sert Shadows Inn

GLEN EDEN SUN CLUB

25999 Glen Eden Road
Corona, CA 91719

CALIFORNIA

909/277-4650

FACILITIES

ACCOMMODATIONS

- ■ Wheelchair Access
- Vacation Villas
- Cabins
- Rooms
- ■ Cable TV
- In-room Telephone
- ■ Trailers
  - ● heated
  - ● w/bath
  - ● cooking
- ■ Restaurant
- Lounge
- Snack Bar
- ■ Store
- ■ Book Store

CAMPING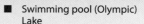

- ■ Tent Spaces
- ■ R/V Spaces
  - ● w/elec
  - ● w/water
  - ● w/sewer
- ■ Disposal Station
- ■ Showers
  - ● cold
  - ● hot
- ■ Laundromat
- Community Kitchen
- ■ Picnic Tables
- ■ Playground
- ■ Pets/Leash only

RECREATION

- ■ Swimming pool (Olympic)
- Lake
- ■ Whirlpool/Spa
- ■ Sauna
- Exercise Equipment
- Tennis
- ■ Volleyball
- ■ Shuffleboard
- ■ Horseshoes
- ■ Pentanque
- Miniten
- Badminton
- Fishing
- ■ Recreation Hall
- ■ Children's Activities
- ■ Teen Activities

■ denotes availability
●
■

INFORMATION

Club Personality
A visitor-friendly resort with a sense of community, Glen Eden is a special place to slip away from the cares of the outside world and relax.
800/843-6833 Information Only
Fax: 909/277-8020
Web site: http://www.gleneden.com

Description of Grounds
One hundred fifty-five acres of private sanctuary with flowers, cactus gardens and lush green lawns posed against the foothills of the Santa Ana Mountains. Complete amenities and leisure activities.

Directions
All major freeways from Los Angeles, Orange or San Diego counties. At Corona, take Interstate 15 south to the Indian Truck Trail exit, turn right one-half block, then left one-half mile to the Glen Eden sign. From the south turn west under the freeway and back south on the service road for one-half mile.

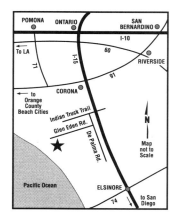

"A special
place to
slip away
from the
cares
of the
outside world."

**Neighboring Sights and
Attractions**
Ideally located within driving distance of
southern California's many attractions—
Disneyland, Tijuana, San Diego, Palm
Springs and Los Angeles. Only one hour
from the beach.

Honored Discounts
Please call for information.

n Eden Sun Club

CALIFORNIA

1631 Harbison Canyon Road
El Cajon, CA 92019

GOLDEN OAKS CLUB

General Information
Golden Oaks Club is family oriented and devoted to sports and social activities. Meetings are held either at a nearby nudist resort or at the home of a member. Various tournaments are held on three-day weekends, and members participate in national and regional activities.

ACTIVITIES & RECREATION

Visits to Nudist Facilities
Tennis
Year-round Activities
Socials
Tournaments

LE CLUB   CALIFORNIA

P.O. Box 19613
San Diego, CA 92159

ACTIVITIES & RECREATION

General Information
A closely knit travel club based at Swallows Sun Island in El Cajon, California.

Volleyball
Tennis
Swimming
Table Tennis
Shuffleboard

CALIFORNIA

**20600 Aldercroft Heights Road
Los Gatos, CA 95030**

LLASA

General Information
A family oriented travel club based at Lupin Naturist Club in Los Gatos, California.

ACTIVITIES & RECREATION

Volleyball
Tennis
Camping
Potlucks
Get-togethers

NAKED VOLLEYBALL

**28175 Via Luis
Laguna Niguel, CA 92677**

CALIFORNIA

714/643-9790

ACTIVITIES & RECREATION

Outdoor Volleyball
Beach Trips
Volleyball Leagues
Regional Nudist Gatherings
Indoor Winter Leagues

Special Events

Visit Glen Eden on the First Sunday of Each Month
Visit McConville on the Third Sunday of Each Month
Annual Meeting at WSA Convention

General Information
Dedicated to Southern California volleyball, club members frequent nudist clubs, clothing-optional beaches, or any other place where a good game and a friendly atmosphere are found. From the newest beginner to the most accomplished player, members are committed to real volleyball.
Web site: http://www.nakedvolleyball.com
E-mail: lenker@earthlink.net

LAGUNA DEL SOL

8683 Rawhide Lane
Wilton, CA 95693

CALIFORNIA

916/687-6550

FACILITIES

ACCOMMODATIONS

- ■ Wheelchair Access
- ■ Vacation Villas (9)
  Cabins
- ■ Rooms (17)
  Cable TV
  In-room Telephone
- ■ Trailers (1)
  - ● heated
  - ● w/bath
  - ● cooking
- ■ Restaurant
- ■ Lounge
  Snack Bar
- ■ Boutique

CAMPING

- ■ Tent Spaces
- ■ R/V Spaces (78)
  - ● w/elec (58)
  - ● w/water (58)
  - ● w/sewer (20)
- ■ Disposal Station
- ■ Showers
  - ● cold (2)
  - ● hot (15)
- ■ Laundromat (2)
  Community Kitchen
- ■ Picnic Tables
- ■ Playground (2)
- ■ Pets/Leash only

RECREATION

- ■ Swimming Pool (3)
- ■ Lake (25-acre)
- ■ Whirlpool/Spa (2)
- ■ Sauna
- ■ Exercise Equipment
- ■ Tennis
- ■ Volleyball
- ■ Shuffleboard
- ■ Horseshoes
  Pentanque
  Miniten
  Badminton
- ■ Fishing
- ■ Recreation Hall
- ■ Children's Activities
- ■ Teen Activities
- ■ Paddleboats, Canoe

■ ● denotes availability

INFORMATION

Club Personality
Laguna del Sol is a year-round destination resort where singles, couples and families are welcomed. Situated at the base of the Sierra Nevada foothills, Laguna del Sol is a lushly landscaped 117-acre resort offering a complete range of facilities and accommodations.
Fax: 916/687-7860
Web site: http://www.lagunadelsol.com

Description of Grounds
The club offers a wonderful mix of unspoiled nature and modern facilities. The 25-acre lake is a central attraction, with waterfront camping, surrounding footpath, boating and fishing. A contemporary two-story entertainment center and lounge features dancing every weekend.

Directions
Highway 99 to Dillard Road then northeast 11 miles to Quince Lane, left to the end of Quince; or Highway 50 to Sunrise Boulevard then south 10 miles to Highway 16, east five miles to Dillard, four miles to Quince Lane, right to the end of Quince.

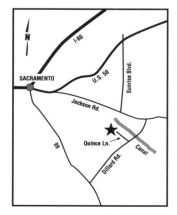

Lag

"A year-round **destination** resort at the base of the **Sierra** Nevada foothills."

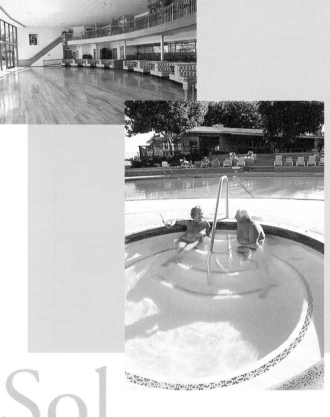

Neighboring Sights and Attractions
Old Sacramento, state capital, gold country, wine country, Lake Tahoe and San Francisco.

Honored Discounts
Discount on grounds fees for AANR and TNS members.

Laguna del Sol

LUPIN NATURIST CLUB

CALIFORNIA

20600 Aldercroft Heights Road
Los Gatos, CA 95030

408/353-2250

FACILITIES

INFORMATION

ACCOMMODATIONS

- Wheelchair Access
  Vacation Villas
- Cabins (1)
- Yurts (7)
- Cable TV
  In-room Telephone
  Trailers
  - heated
  - w/bath
  - cooking
- Restaurant
- Lounge
- Snack Bar
- Store

CAMPING

- Tent Spaces (65)
- R/V Spaces
  - w/elec
  - w/water
  - w/sewer
  Disposal Station
- Showers
  - cold (2)
  - hot (5)
  Laundromat
- Community Kitchen
- Picnic Tables (10)
- Playground
- Pets/Leash only

RECREATION

- Swimming Pool (2)
  Lake
- Whirlpool/Spa (2)
- Sauna
- Exercise Equipment
- Tennis
- Volleyball
- Shuffleboard
- Horseshoes
  Pentanque
  Miniten
  Badminton
  Fishing
- Recreation Hall
- Children's Activities
  Teen Activities
- ■ Nature Trail, Massage

● denotes availability
■

Club Personality
Located on the sunny slopes of the scenic Santa Cruz Mountains, Lupin serves a cosmopolitan membership of over 1,000 San Francisco Bay Area families, couples and singles of all ages. Visitors, especially first-timers, are welcome.
Fax: 408/353-2230
Web site: http://www.lupin.com
E-mail: office@lupin.com

Description of Grounds

The 110-acre wooded grounds contain an upper activities area for sports and family play, a lower quiet area for simple relaxation, and a one-mile nature trail. Beautiful trees, green lawns, blue pools, sunny decks and natural rock gardens abound. The Clubhouse Restaurant also serves as an art gallery and weekend entertainment center.

Neighboring Sights and Attractions
Within a one hour drive are San Francisco, Silicon Valley, San Jose, Great America, Monterey Bay, Santa Cruz, nude beaches, and old growth redwoods. San Jose Airport is about 15 miles away.

Honored Discounts
Preferred rates for AANR, INF, NNC, Naturist Society and recognized club members.

Directions
Call or write for information and directions before visiting.

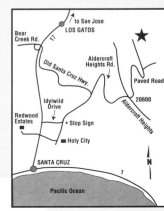

FACILITIES

ACCOMMODATIONS

- ■ Wheelchair Access
  Vacation Villas
  Trailers
  Rooms
  Cable TV
  In-room Telephone
- ■ Cabins (45)
  - ● heated
  - ● w/bath
  - ● cooking
  Restaurant
- ■ Lounge
  Snack Bar
  Store

CAMPING

- ■ Tent Spaces (50)
- ■ R/V Spaces (20)
  w/elec
  - ● w/water (10)
  w/sewer
  Disposal Station
- ■ Showers
  cold
  - ● hot (5)
  Laundromat
  Community Kitchen
- ■ Picnic Tables (10)
- ■ Playground
- ■ Pets/Leash only

RECREATION

- ■ Swimming Pool (34' x 62')
  Lake
  Whirlpool/Spa
  Sauna
- ■ Exercise Equipment
- ■ Tennis
- ■ Volleyball
- ■ Shuffleboard
- ■ Horseshoes
  Pentanque
  Miniten
- ■ Badminton
  Fishing
- ■ Recreation Hall
- ■ Children's Activities
  Teen Activities
- ■
- ■ 10' Wading Pool

■ denotes availability

INFORMATION

Club Personality
McConville is one of the friendliest clubs in Southern California. Activities are centered around down-home entertainment and get-togethers like potlucks and dances, together with sports, swimming, and relaxing in the sun.

Description of Grounds
McConville is located on the ocean side of the coastal mountain range, in the heart of the Cleveland National Forest. Temperatures are mild both winter and summer in this beautiful oak-and-sycamore-lined canyon which comes complete with a seasonal creek. 45 cabins are individually nestled through the canyon among the trees on 129 acres. Hiking trails are on the grounds.

Neighboring Sights and Attractions
Approximately 75 miles to Los Angeles and San Diego; 45 miles to Disneyland; 27 miles to the Pacific Ocean and to Dana Point Harbor, fishing and museum; 7.5 miles to Lake Elsinore for water skiing, fishing, or antique shopping; 30 miles to Temecula's wine country.

Honored Discounts
Discounts on gate fees to all AANR and national nudist organization members.

Directions
Inland from I-15 or I-215, take Highway 74 west to Lake Elsinore. The Ortega Highway, starting from where the Elsinore Valley, crosses the coastal mountain range to San Juan Capistrano. Go 6.5 miles up the mountain to the Los Pinos Camp Road, make a right turn and continue for 3/4 of a mile to a dirt fork. Make a right turn and go 600 feet to the McConville gate.

From the coast on I-5, proceed to San Juan Capistrano to Highway 74. 21.5 miles inland, make a left turn on Los Pinos Camp Road, then follow directions as above.

CALIFORNIA

209/265-7422

NATURAL MANNER CLUB

P.O. Box 1560
Reedley, CA 93654-1560

General Information
Natural Manner Club of Central California is a nonlanded, family oriented nudist club serving central California from Bakersfield to Modesto. The club maintains an active year-round schedule of activities which encourage family participation, including local events and travel to nearby areas. To learn more about the club and upcoming activities visit its web site at: http://www.naturists.com/nmc/ E-mail: clauser@worldnet.att.net

 ACTIVITIES & RECREATION

Potluck Dinners
Trips to Ocean, Lake Beaches and Mountains
Pool Parties and Hot Tubbing
Dances
Trips to Nearby Landed Clubs
Holiday Celebrations

Special Events
Annual Chili Cook-off
Oktoberfest
Spring Wildflower Hike

THE OLYMPIAN CLUB

P.O. Box 819
Bellflower, CA 90707

CALIFORNIA

562/424-0354

ACTIVITIES & RECREATION

Beach Trips
Resort Visits
Potluck Dinners
Special Interest Groups

General Information
The Olympian Club is a nonlanded travel club providing members with a heavy schedule of indoor and outdoor activities, primarily in the Greater Los Angeles area. Membership is open to persons of all ages and ethnic backgrounds interested in social nude recreation. Known euphemistically as "an eating club," the Olympians' credo is "Good Times Naturally."
E-mail: olympnclub@aol.com

Special Events
Annual Installation Dinner/Dance in January
Memorial Day Weekend Anniversary at Silver Valley Sun Club
Labor Day Weekend Celebration at Olive Dell Ranch

OLIVE DELL RANCH

**26520 Keissel Road
Colton, CA 92324-9526**

CALIFORNIA
909/825-6619

FACILITIES

ACCOMMODATIONS

- ■ Wheelchair Access (limited)
  Vacation Villas
- ■ Cabins (6)
  Rooms
  Cable TV
  In-room Telephone
  Trailers
     heated
     w/bath
     cooking
- ■ Restaurant
  Lounge
  Snack Bar
  Store

CAMPING

- ■ Tent Spaces (10)
- ■ R/V Spaces (32)
  - ● w/elec (22)
  - ● w/water (22)
     w/sewer
- ■ Disposal Station
- ■ Showers
  - ● cold (6)
  - ● hot (5)
  Laundromat
  Community Kitchen
- ■ Picnic Tables
- ■ Playground
  Pets/Leash Only

RECREATION

- ■ Swimming Pool (24' x 48')
  Lake
- ■ Whirlpool/Spa
- ■ Sauna
  Exercise Equipment
- ■ Tennis
- ■ Volleyball
- ■ Shuffleboard
- ■ Horseshoes
  Pentanque
  Miniten
- ■ Badminton
  Fishing
- ■ Recreation Hall
- ■ Children's Activities
  Teen Activities
- ■ Horseback Riding

■ ● denotes availability

INFORMATION

Club Personality
Nestled among sheltering semidesert hills which provide smog-free weather, Olive Dell Ranch has been offering an ideal year-round climate for enjoyment of the outdoors since 1952. Among the many available pastimes are hiking, parties, volleyball, potlucks, billiards, and horseback riding, by arrangement, for experienced equestrians.
E-mail: kilborn@earthlink.net

Description of Grounds
Situated in Southern California, Olive Dell Ranch comprises 145 acres of semidesert country, 2,000 feet high. Accommodations include 6 heated cabins with linens, 10 tent sites and 22 RV sites with electric and water hookups. Also on the premises is a self-guided hiking trail, very large whirlpool/spa, and children's playground.

Neighboring Sights and Attractions
Olive Dell Ranch is only one hour from **Disneyland** and **Knott's Berry Farm** to the west, and **Palm Springs** to the east. Ontario International Airport is 40 miles away. San Bernardino and Moreno Valley, both 6 miles away, provide goods and services to meet any need.

Honored Discounts
Discounts for AANR, TNS, and other recognized nudist organization members.

Directions
From Ontario International Airport use Interstate 10 east toward San Bernardino. Take the 215 Freeway south to the first exit, Washington Street/Mt. Vernon Avenue. Turn right and take Washington Street east to Reche Canyon Road. Go south on Reche Canyon for five-plus miles and turn left onto Keissel Road, which ends at Olive Dell's gate. Landmarks include the Reche Canyon Mobile Home Park and the Hitchin Post Market.

CALIFORNIA

919/880-0803

Club Personality
Open year-round, Buff Creek Nudist Resort is a portal to the world of nude living and recreation. Buff Creek is a couples and family resort with sports and relaxation facilities.

Description of Grounds
The resort is situated on 40 private acres nestled up to the National Forest among tall pines in rural Southern California.

Neighboring Sights and Attractions
All within a short drive are the Blockbusters Pavilion, Pharaoh's Lost Kingdom, Raging Waters, Disneyland, Universal Studios, wineries, Lake Arrowhead, Hollywood and local museums.

BUFF CREEK NUDIST RESORT

1924 Glen Helen Road
Devore, CA 92407

 ACCOMMODATIONS & RECREATION

Restaurant and Relaxation Center
Swimming Pool (30' x 60') with Deck
Indoor and Outdoor Jacuzzis
Sauna and Steam Room
Lighted Tennis and Volleyball Courts
Mobile Home and RV Sites
Rental Units
Snack Bar and Mini-Mart
Hiking and Jogging Trails

SANROBLES

P.O. Box 4763
Hayward, CA 94540

ACTIVITIES & RECREATION

Visiting Landed Clubs
Year-round House Parties
Pool/Spa Gatherings
Weekend Getaways

CALIFORNIA

510/743-1223

General Information
A family travel club that visits landed clubs on holidays and other occasions. At least once a month there is a special event—such as a pool, barbecue, or spa party—where members, prospective members and guests enjoy each other's company. Families and singles are welcomed at Sanrobles.

Special Events
Reno/Las Vegas Trips
Houseboat Trips
Beach Gatherings
Annual Membership Meeting
Annual Birthday Party in March

CALIFORNIA

10200 Cull Canyon Road
Castro Valley, CA 94546

510/582-0194

FACILITIES

ACCOMMODATIONS

Wheelchair Access
Vacation Villas
Cabins
Rooms
Cable TV
In-room Telephone
Trailers
    heated
    w/bath
    cooking
Restaurant
Lounge
Snack Bar
Store

CAMPING

■ Tent Spaces
■ R/V Spaces
  ● w/elec (7)
  ● w/water (7)
    w/sewer
  Disposal Station
■ Showers
  ● cold
  ● hot
  Laundromat
■ Community Kitchen
■ Picnic Tables
■ Playground
■ Pets/Leash only

RECREATION

■ Swimming Pool
  Lake
■ Whirlpool/Spa
  Sauna
  Exercise Equipment
  Tennis
■ Volleyball
■ Shuffleboard
■ Horseshoes
  Pentanque
  Miniten
■ Badminton
  Fishing
■ Recreation Hall
  Children's Activities
  Teen Activities
■ Hiking

● denotes availability
■

INFORMATION

Club Personality
Sequoians' members are married, single, young, old, with and without children. The group practices social nude recreation in a family oriented environment. Members respect and appreciate each other's diversity. Favorite activities include barbecues, potlucks, dances, hiking, holiday parties and just plain relaxing.
800/404-6833
Web site: http://www.ihot.com/~sequoian/

Description of Grounds
The Sequoians is a rustic, family oriented nudist club located nine miles northeast of Castro Valley, California. The grounds are heavily wooded with oaks, madrones, bay laurels and redwoods. The club is located in a quiet and sheltered box canyon—the perfect place to enjoy nude recreation in an unspoiled natural setting.

Neighboring Sights and Attractions
The Central Bay Area location allows easy visits to several popular sites including Napa Wine Country, Silicon Valley, Santa Cruz Boardwalk, and all of San Francisco including Fisherman's Wharf, Alcatraz, Golden Gate Park, and the Castro District.

Honored Discounts
Discounts to AANR, The Naturist Society, and International Naturist Federation members.

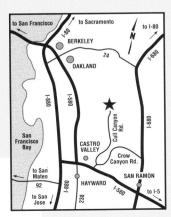

Directions
Interstate 580 to Castro Valley, Crow Canyon Road, exit and follow Crow Canyon about 0.5 miles, turn left onto Cull Canyon Road. I-680 to San Ramon, Crow Canyon Road, exit and drive 7.9 miles west. North on Cull Canyon Road. 6.5 miles to the end. Take the right-hand gravel road and bear right past horse corral to the club's road. From the large hanging Sequoian's sign, the office and gate are 0.4 miles.

CALIFORNIA

P.O. Box 7842
Van Nuys, CA 91409

PACIFICANS

General Information
Members of the Pacificans are couples who live throughout Southern California. Historically, the club has remained small in number but large in spirit. Write to the Pacificans for more information.

ACTIVITIES & RECREATION

Camp Outs at Nudist Campgrounds
Houseboat, RV, and Ski Trips
Beach and House Parties

WEE BEAR CLUB

CALIFORNIA

P.O. Box 710088
Santee, CA 92072-0088

ACTIVITIES & RECREATION

Trips to Nudist Facilities
Picnics
Meetings
Social Gatherings

General Information
A travel club that has been serving the Greater San Diego Area since 1963. Inquiries are invited from folks interested in learning more about family oriented nude activities. Couples and singles are welcome.

SILVER VALLEY SUN CLUB

48382 Silver Valley Road
Newberry Springs, CA 92365

CALIFORNIA

760/257-4239

FACILITIES

ACCOMMODATIONS

- ■ Wheelchair Access
  Vacation Villas
  Cabins
- ■ Rooms (3)
  Cable TV
  In-room Telephone
- ■ Trailers (3)
  - ● heated
    w/bath
  - ● cooking
    Restaurant
    Lounge
- ■ Snack Bar
  Store

CAMPING

- ■ Tent Spaces (12)
- ■ R/V Spaces
  - ● w/elec (16)
  - ● w/water (16)
    w/sewer
- ■ Disposal Station
- ■ Showers
  - ● cold
  - ● hot (6)
    Laundromat
    Community Kitchen
- ■ Picnic Tables (7)
- ■ Playground
- ■ Pets/Leash only

RECREATION

  Swimming Pool
- ■ Lake (2.5 acre)
- ■ Whirlpool/Spa
  Sauna
  Exercise Equipment
  Tennis
  Volleyball
- ■ Shuffleboard
- ■ Horseshoes
  Pentanque
  Miniten
  Badminton
- ■ Fishing
  Recreation Hall
  Children's Activities
  Teen Activities

■ ● denotes availability
■

INFORMATION

Club Personality
Warm and friendly, with a family atmosphere. Located in the Mojave Desert, between I-15 and I-40. Open all year.

Description of Grounds
Clean, with a tree-lined lake complete with two islands. Sun or shade all day, as desired.

Neighboring Sights and Attractions
Within minutes of the new Mojave National Preserve, Calico Ghost Town, The Early Man Site, and desert hiking trails.

Honored Discounts
Discounts for AANR, TNS and INF members. Special November-through-April discounts for snowbirds.

Directions
Located eight to 11 miles off Interstates 15 or 40. From Los Angeles take I-40 east to Newberry Springs exit. From Bakersfield, I-15 east to Harvard Road exit. From Las Vegas, I-15 west to Harvard Road exit. From Arizona, I-40 west to Ft. Cady/Newberry Springs exit. Follow map to Newberry Road, turn east at the school onto Silver Valley Road, three and one-third miles to gate on left. All roads are paved.

FACILITIES

ACCOMMODATIONS

Wheelchair Access
Vacation Villas
Cabins
- Rooms (10)
- Air Conditioned
- Cable TV
Trailers
   heated
   w/bath
   cooking
Restaurant
Lounge
- Snack Bar
Store

CAMPING

- Tent Spaces
- R/V Spaces (20)
  - w/elec
  - w/water
  - w/sewer
- Disposal Station
- Showers
  - cold
  - hot
- Laundromat
- Community Kitchen
- Picnic Tables
- Playground
- Pets

RECREATION

- Swimming Pool
- Lake
- Whirlpool/Spa
- Sauna
- Exercise Equipment
- Tennis
- Volleyball
- Shuffleboard
- Horseshoes
- Bocce Ball
- Miniten
- Badminton
- Fishing
- Recreation Hall
- Children's Activities
- Teen Activities

■ ● denotes availability
■

INFORMATION

Club Personality

This 20-acre park is nestled in the canyon about 25 miles from San Diego. Two thriving communities are 7 miles in either direction. San Diego County's only nudist resort offers the ultimate in year-round weather.
Web Site: http://www.swallowssunilsland.com
E-mail: Jshafer@znet.com

Description of Grounds

RV sites, tent spaces and overnight rooms are available. Showers, laundromat, restaurant, community kitchen and playground are conveniently located. Within driving distance of the grounds are Southern California's Glen Eden, McConville, Olive Dell and Silver Valley Sun Club.

Neighboring Sights and Attractions

The San Diego Zoo, Sea World, Wild Animal Park, The Convention Center, Black's Beach, and Mexico are just a few of the sights to be seen within a short drive.

Directions

Go east from San Diego on Highway 8 to El Cajon Boulevard. In El Cajon go to second traffic light and turn right on Washington. Go to the end of the street, approximately three miles, continue on Dehesa Road. Five miles out Dehesa Road you come to Harbison Canyon Road, remain on the road. The club is three-quarters of a mile up the road on the right-hand side.

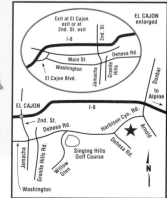

THE TERRA COTTA INN

2388 East Racquet Club Road
Palm Springs, CA 92262

CALIFORNIA

800/786-6938

INFORMATION

General Information

For natural fun and sun, the preferred choice is The Terra Cotta Inn—featured travel destination in *Los Angeles Magazine,* Best of L.A. issue. Be pampered in a luxurious resort for couples that features spacious rooms, a beautiful private garden, lovely pool, breathtaking mountain views, sumptuous homemade breakfasts and spa services.

Luxurious and affordable.
Phone: 800/786-6938 or 760/322-6059
Web Site:
http://www.ernestallen.com/tr/ca/theterracottainn

THE Terra Cotta INN

ACCOMMODATIONS & AMENITIES

- 17 Luxuriously Appointed, Spacious Rooms
- Kitchens and Private Patios Available
- Heated Pool and Large Outdoor Jacuzzi Spa
- Poolside Breakfasts and Afternoon Refreshments Included
- Catered Lunches Available
- On-Staff Massage Therapist
- Full Spa Amenities
- Mid-Week and Weekly Specials

Neighboring Sites and Attractions

Just steps away, Palm Springs offers a wide variety of dining, shopping, cultural and recreational activities. Championship golf is nearby. San Diego, Disneyland and Los Angeles make comfortable day trips.

Honored Discounts

Discounts provided for members of AANR, TNS, INF and CCBN.

Directions

From 10 eastbound, Exit Highway 111 Palm Springs. Turn left at the second light in town onto Racquet Club Road. Go east 1.7 miles to 2388 E. Racquet Club Road.

MOUNTAIN AIR RANCH

P.O. Box 855
Indian Hills, CO 80455

COLORADO

303/697-4083

FACILITIES

ACCOMMODATIONS

Wheelchair Access
Vacation Villas
■ Cabins (3)
Rooms
Cable TV
In-room Telephone
■ Trailers (1)
  ● heated
  ● w/bath
  ● cooking
■ Restaurant (Weekends)
Lounge
Snack Bar
Store
■ Ice Cream Parlor (Weekends)

CAMPING

■ Tent Spaces (15-20)
■ R/V Spaces (15)
  ● w/elec (15)
  ● w/water (15)
  w/sewer
■ Disposal Station
■ Showers
  cold
  ● hot (6)
  Laundromat
■ Community Kitchen
■ Picnic Tables (18)
■ Playground
■ Pets/Leash only

RECREATION

■ Swimming Pool (25' x 50')
■ Pool Slide
■ Whirlpool/Spa
■ Sauna
  Exercise Equipment
■ Tennis (Platform)
■ Volleyball
■ Shuffleboard
■ Horseshoes
■ Boccee Ball
  Miniten
  Badminton
  Fishing
■ Recreation Hall
■ Children's Activities
■ Kid's Playroom
■ Teen Activities

● denotes availability
■

INFORMATION

Club Personality
Voted by visitors—in both 1995 and 1996—as the friendliest club in the U.S. and Canada, Mountain Air Ranch is a family oriented resort with couples and singles of all ages and backgrounds. In operation for over 60 years, it is one of the oldest clubs around. Visitors must arrive between 10 a.m. and 6 p.m.
Web Site: http://www.earthlink.net/~tanis2/

Description of Grounds
Situated on 150 acres of Denver foothills, the ranch has ten miles of groomed hiking trails, as well as a large swimming pool, hot tub, sauna and a clubhouse where monthly dances with live bands are featured. Special kids' room and playground. Sports activities include volleyball, paddle tennis, bocce ball, shuffleboard, and horseshoes. Guests, at their own discretion, may sleep in a cabin, camp in a tent meadow, or hook up an RV.

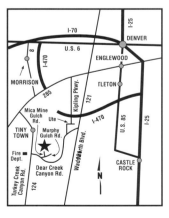

Directions
Please call in advance. Approximately 25 miles southwest of Denver.

Mc

"**Voted** by visitors the **friendliest** club in the U.S. and Canada."

Neighboring Sights and Attractions
One-half hour from Denver, one hour from Colorado Springs, 40 minutes from Central City casinos, and within two hours of five ski areas.

Honored Discounts
20 percent discount on grounds fees to AANR and The Naturist Society members.

untain Air Ranch

COLORADO

303/420-4565

ROCKY MOUNTAIN BARES

P.O. Box 740159
Arvada, CO 80006

ACTIVITIES & RECREATION

General Information
Rocky Mountain Bares is a nonlanded club. Activities are on a scheduled basis. Please contact Rocky Mountain Bares in advance for a schedule and location of events.
E-mail: rmbnickrson@msn.com

Swim Parties and Socials at Local Health Club
Backyard Barbecues and Pool Parties
Potlucks
House Parties
Camping
Hiking

GARDEN OF EDEN

P.O. Box 15
Plymouth, CT 06782-0015

CONNECTICUT

860/283-5846

ACTIVITIES & RECREATION

Visits to Nudist Parks
Camping
Potluck Dinners
Holiday Parties
Swims at Local Health Club
Hot Tubbing
Beach Gatherings

General Information
The Garden of Eden is a nonlanded club which travels the Northeast to local landed clubs, beaches and other destinations during the summer. Members meet during the winter months as well. The Garden of Eden welcomes singles, couples and families. Please send a legal size, self-addressed, stamped envelope for more information.
Fax: 860/283-0453
E-mail: 75031.1453@Compuserve.com

FACILITIES

ACCOMMODATIONS

- ■ Wheelchair Access (1)
- Vacation Villas
- ■ Cabins (5)
- ■ Rooms (5)
- Cable TV
- In-room Telephone
- Trailers
  - heated
  - w/bath
  - cooking
- Restaurant
- Lounge
- ■ Snack Bar
- Store

CAMPING

- ■ Tent Spaces (20)
- ■ R/V Spaces (25)
  - ● w/elec (25)
  - ● w/water (25)
  - w/sewer
- ■ Disposal Station
- ■ Showers
  - ● cold (14)
  - ● hot (13)
- ■ Laundromat
- Community Kitchen
- ■ Picnic Tables (40)
- ■ Playground
- ■ Pets/Leash only

RECREATION

- ■ Swimming Pool (30' x 60')
- ■ Lake (4 Acre)
- ■ Whirlpool/Spa
- ■ Sauna
- ■ Exercise Equipment
- ■ Tennis
- ■ Volleyball
- ■ Shuffleboard
- ■ Horseshoes
- ■ Pentanque
- Miniten
- ■ Badminton
- ■ Fishing
- ■ Boating
- ■ Recreation Hall
- ■ Children's Activities
- ■ Teen Activities

■ denotes availability

INFORMATION

Club Personality
Since its founding in 1934, Solair has grown steadily through the years. Although there have been many additions to the facilities in recent years, Solair continues to be a place of rustic charm.
Web Site: http://www.neca.com/~solair/
Fax: 860/928-4709   E-mail: solair@neca.com

Description of Grounds
Solair is situated on 350 wooded acres in northeastern Connecticut, with miles of hiking trails. There is a lake for swimming, boating and fishing, as well as a heated pool, hot tub and sauna.

Neighboring Sights and Attractions
Solair is only four miles from major shopping and dining. Nearby attractions include Boston, Mystic Seaport, Newport, Foxwood Casino, Old Sturbridge Village and The Ledges.

Honored Discounts
Discounts to AANR and TNS members.

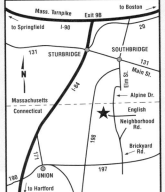

Directions
From Interstate 90, take Sturbridge Exit 9B. Left onto Route 131 east, 4.5 miles to Southbridge. Turn right onto Elm Street and 198. After one-half mile, bear left at the fork, leaving 198. After another mile, go right on Alpine Drive for 2.7 miles. At the intersection of English Neighborhood Road turn right onto the dirt road. Call or write for detailed directions.

CONNECTICUT

860/779-1512

Club Personality
A family oriented club situated on 36 private acres nestled on a mountain ridge in rural Connecticut.

Description of Grounds
Open May 15 through October 15. RV Sites with electric and water, and a disposal station are available, as well as safari tent sites in a lovely pine grove. A large open sunning area surrounds the pool with a pavilion for outdoor functions.

Neighboring Sites and Attractions
Within reasonable driving distance of the Connecticut casinos, Mystic Seaport and Aquarium, Old Sturbridge Village, and the Newport mansions.

SUN RIDGE RESORT

131 Calvin French Road
Sterling, CT 06377

 ACCOMMODATIONS & RECREATION

Camping, RV Sites with Hookups
Swimming Pool (24' x 60')
20' Heated Conversation Pool
Rental Trailers
Snack Bar and Store
Two Paved Tennis Courts
Recreation Hall
Children's Playground

DELMARVA SUNCATCHERS

P.O. Box 321
Nassau, DE 19969

DELAWARE

302/644-2254

 ACTIVITIES & RECREATION

Monthly Events at Landed Clubs
or Members' Homes.

General Information
Delmarva Suncatchers is a nudist club serving the Delaware, Maryland, Virginia area. Members enjoy year-round activities at landed clubs or members' homes.
E-mail: delmarva.suncatchers@dol.net

CENTRAL FLORIDA NATURISTS

P.O. Box 2004
Merritt Island, FL 32954-2004

FLORIDA

407/381-0637

ACTIVITIES & RECREATION

General Members Meeting on
First Wednesday of Every Month
House and Pool Parties
Card, Massage, and Cooking
Groups Meet Throughout
the Month
Clothing and
Blood Drives

Special Events
Clothing-Optional Bowling
Superbowl Parties
Beach Cookouts

General Information
Central Florida Naturists, founded in
1992, is a nonprofit organization dedicated to the preservation of Playalinda
and Apollo as clothing-optional beaches
within the Canaveral National Seashore.
The club is affiliated with The Naturist
Society, and holds an affiliate charter as a
nonlanded club with AANR. Central
Florida Naturists, a wholesome family
oriented club, is open to singles, couples
and families. Members come from many
backgrounds, and represent various
professions, skills, and political, social and
religious affiliations.
Fax: 407/381-0637
Web Site: http://nebula.ispace.com/cfn

FLORIDA

904/636-7900

NORTHEAST FLORIDA NATURISTS

5800 University Boulevard, W. #537
Jacksonville, FL 32216

General Information
Northeast Florida Naturists is a
not-for-profit, nonlanded, family
oriented travel club interested
in a more relaxing way of life.
An informative newsletter
covering club activities and the
activities of other clubs is
available to members on a
monthly basis.
E-mail: NFNaturists@juno.com

Holiday Parties
Monthly Meetings and Socials
Visits to Nudist Parks

Special Events
Memorial Day Pig Roast at Cypress Cove
Houseboat Cruise
Fish Fry
Halloween Party
Thanksgiving Dinner

CALIENTE

6500 Land O'Lakes Blvd. (US 41 N.)
Land O'Lakes, FL 34639

FLORIDA

813/996-3700

INFORMATION

ACCOMMODATIONS

Caliente Resort is a major new nude recreation club, destination resort and residential community which is under construction as this publication goes to press. The planned opening date for limited operation is late 1997, with full services and activities in 1998.
The 96-acre site, 20 miles north of Tampa, Florida, features two lakes with white sand beaches, nature preserves, and mature trees. Caliente will have vacation cottages, hotel rooms, six tennis courts, three heated swimming pools, water and beach volleyball, petanque, shuffleboard and horseshoes, several bars and restaurants, an exercise studio, and shops.

RECREATION/RESIDENTIAL

Club Caliente will offer an extensive series of social programs, dances, sports tournaments, theme parties, festivals and special events.

The community's residential sections will have apartments, townhouses and single family homes. Please contact Caliente for up-to-date information.
Mailing Address: P.O. Box 1255, Land O'Lakes, FL 34639
Toll Free: 800/326-7731   Fax: 813/949-3616

Best Airport
Tampa International, 20 miles;
St. Petersburg/Clearwater International also has major airline service and is about 10 miles farther.

Directions
From downtown Tampa, from St. Petersburg, or from either airport, take I-275 north, through Tampa to Bearss Ave. exit, then east one block to U.S. 41. Follow U.S. 41 eleven miles through Lutz and Land O'Lakes to Caliente at 6500 Land O'Lakes Blvd. (U.S. 41 N.)

From Orlando-Kissimmee area, take I-4 west to I-75, then north on I-75 to Highway 54 (Land O'Lakes exit), then west on Highway 54 to U.S. 41, and north on U.S. 41 to Caliente.

From the Gulf Coast, follow U.S. 19 to Highway 54, then east on Highway 54 to U.S. 41, and go north to Caliente.

From the north, exit I-75 at Highway 52, then go west on Highway 52 to U.S. 41. Turn south on U.S. 41 to Caliente.

"A perfectly **natural** community in the **heart** of *nudist country.*"

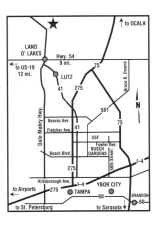

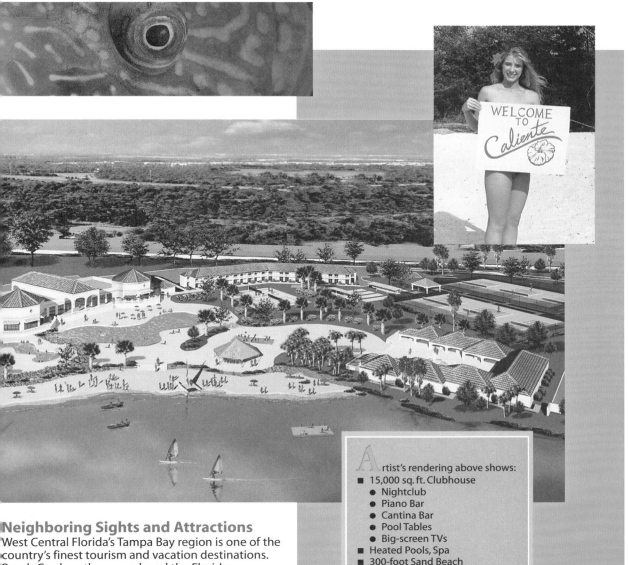

Neighboring Sights and Attractions

West Central Florida's Tampa Bay region is one of the country's finest tourism and vacation destinations. Busch Gardens theme park and the Florida Aquarium, major league baseball, NFL football, and NHL hockey, beautiful Gulf beaches, and quaint ethnic communities (Ybor City, Tarpon Springs) are within minutes. There are 27 golf courses within 30 minutes. Central Florida's major attractions—Disney World, Epcot, Universal Studios, Sea World, MGM, and Cypress Gardens—are an easy day-trip.

Honored Discounts

Discounts for AANR, TNS and INF members.

Artist's rendering above shows:
- 15,000 sq. ft. Clubhouse
  - Nightclub
  - Piano Bar
  - Cantina Bar
  - Pool Tables
  - Big-screen TVs
- Heated Pools, Spa
- 300-foot Sand Beach
- Beach Bar
- Tennis Club With Championship Quality, "Cushion" Courts
- Sports Courts
- Shops, Boutiques

Caliente
RESORT
A Perfectly Natural Community

CLUB PARADISE

P.O. Box 750
Land O'Lakes, FL 34639

FLORIDA

813/949-9327

INFORMATION

Paradise Lakes . . . Where the People are as Warm as the Florida Sun.

ACCOMMODATIONS

This is a vast resort complex with more than 100 accommodations of several different varieties which include poolside hotel rooms, studio condos, cottages, vacation condos and two bedroom condos. Many of these have kitchen facilities. There is also a tenting area, 60 RV sites, available with full hookups, picnic tables, showers and laundromat. Additionally, there is a nightclub, restaurant, snack bar, outdoor bar, retail stores and boutiques, showers, sauna, beauty salon and massage therapists.

Club Personality

Club Paradise is the North America's largest clothing optional resort located on 72.5 acres in Land O'Lakes, Florida, 17 miles north of Tampa International Airport and within a 90-minute drive from Orlando. The setting combines tropical beauty with luxury in a unique 40 million dollar club and residential community. Club Paradise boasts 550 year-round residents, and more than 5,700 members.
Outside Florida: 800/237-2226
Fax: 813/949-1008
Web Site:
http//www.paradiselakes.com

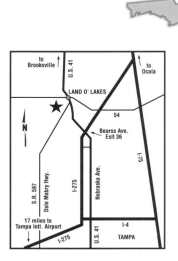

Directions:

Seventeen miles north of Tampa International Airport at the intersection of Dale Mabry Highway (S.R. 597) and U.S. 41 in Land O'Lakes.

Club Parad

"Club Paradise is

The Ultimate

in fun, excitement,

adventure and

romance."

Amenities and activities include dances, sports and entertainment daily, one indoor and two outdoor swimming pools, two water volleyball pools, two hot tubs, one large 72-foot jet pool, putt-putt golf, shuffleboard, horseshoes, three lighted sand volleyball courts, five tennis courts, pool, daily wand exercise classes and a weight room.

ise at Paradise Lakes

CYPRESS COVE

4425 Pleasant Hill Road
Kissimmee, FL 34746

FLORIDA

407/933-5870

FACILITIES

ACCOMMODATIONS

- ■ Wheelchair Access
- ■ Vacation Villas (36)
  Cabins
- ■ Rooms (48)
- ■ Cable TV
- ■ In-room Telephone
  Trailers
    heated
    w/bath
    cooking
- ■ Restaurant
- ■ Lounge
- ■ Snack Bar
- ■ Store

CAMPING

- ■ Tent Spaces
- ■ R/V Spaces (100)
  - ● w/elec
  - ● w/water
  - ● w/sewer
- ■ Disposal Station
- ■ Showers
  - ● cold (20)
  - ● hot (17)
- ■ Laundromat
  Community Kitchen
- ■ Picnic Tables (100)
- ■ Playground
- ■ Pets/Leash only

RECREATION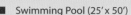

- ■ Swimming Pool (25' x 50')
- ■ Lake (50 acre)
- ■ Whirlpool/Spa
  Sauna
  Exercise Equipment
- ■ Tennis
- ■ Volleyball
- ■ Shuffleboard
- ■ Horseshoes
- ■ Petanque
- ■ Miniten
  Badminton
- ■ Fishing
- ■ Recreation Hall
- ■ Children/Teen Activities
- ■ 9-hole Chip and Putt Course
- ■ Water Sports

■ ● denotes availability

INFORMATION

Club Personality
A family resort with regular activities for children and adults. Relaxing, stress-free environment for those who enjoy quiet and nature, as well as numerous events, sports activities, and opportunities for socializing.
Toll Free: 888/683-3120.
Fax: 407/933-3559
Web Site: http://www.suncove.com
E-mail: cypcove@suncove.com

Description of Grounds
Experience life as nature intended. Relax and enjoy nearly 300 acres of unspoiled wilderness with all the amenities of a fine resort. Hotel, restaurant, Cheeks bar and grill, swimming pool, tennis, volleyball, petanque, shuffleboard, darts, ping pong, playground, 50-acre lake for fishing and boating, and a nine hole chip 'n' putt golf course.

Directions: From the Orlando Airport take 528 West to John Young Parkway, then turn left (south) to Kissimmee. John Young Parkway becomes Bermuda Avenue in Kissimmee. Take Bermuda Avenue straight through Kissimmee, to about $2^{1}/_{2}$ miles out of town. Turn left onto Pleasant Hill Road and proceed south a little over seven miles to the club's gate, on the left.

From U.S. 192 West or the Disney World area, take Poinciana Boulevard south to Pleasant Hill Road, then left one-quarter mile to the club's gate, on the right.

Guests arriving from other directions can phone 407/933-5870. After office hours, phone the gate attendant at 407/933-4011.

"Nude recreation **shines** in this **star** attraction."

Neighboring Sights and Attractions
Within a 45-minute drive of Walt Disney World, Disney MGM Studios, Sea World, Universal Studios, Cypress Gardens, Splendid China, and Church Street Station.

Honored Discounts
Discounts for AANR, TNS, and INF members.

ress Cove

53

GULF COAST RESORT

13220 Houston Avenue
Hudson, FL 34667-6101

FLORIDA

813/868-1061

FACILITIES

ACCOMMODATIONS

- Wheelchair Access
- ■ Vacation Villas (3)
- Cabins
- ■ Rooms (6)
- ■ Cable TV
- In-room Telephone
- ■ Trailers (10)
  - ● heated (10)
  - w/bath
  - ● cooking (10)
- ■ Restaurant
- ■ Lounge
- ■ Snack Bar
- ■ Store

CAMPING

- ■ Tent Spaces (20)
- ■ R/V Spaces (50)
- ■ ● w/elec (50)
- ■ ● w/water (50)
- ● w/sewer (30)
- ■ Disposal Station
- ■ Showers
  - ● cold (10)
  - ● hot (8)
- ■ Laundromat
- Community Kitchen
- ■ Picnic Tables (50)
- ■ Playground
- ■ Pets/Leash only

RECREATION

- ■ Swimming Pool (20'x40')
- Lake
- ■ Whirlpool/Spa
- Sauna
- Exercise Equipment
- ■ Tennis
- ■ Volleyball
- ■ Shuffleboard
- ■ Horseshoes
- ■ Petanque
- Miniten
- Badminton
- Fishing
- ■ Recreation Hall
- Children's Activities
- Teen Activities

■ ● denotes availability

INFORMATION

Club Personality
Gulf Coast Resort, a friendly place for playing or relaxing, welcomes young couples, families and seniors.

Description of Grounds
A very rustic, tranquil setting on 40 wooded acres. Shaded RV sites with 20, 30, or 50 amps.

Neighboring Sights and Attractions
Located in Hudson, Florida, just one hour from Tampa and two hours from Orlando. Attractions, shopping and restaurants are within a 3 to 8 mile radius. Gulf beaches are 15 to 30 miles away.

Honored Discounts
Discounts for AANR, and INF members. Please call for information on other discounts.

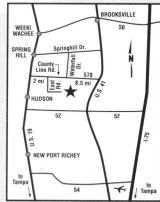

Directions
Route 19 or U.S. 41, north from Tampa to Pasco/Hernando County line (Route 578). From Rt. 19, go two and one-half miles; from U.S. 41 go eight and one-half miles. Watch for the Citco gas station on the south side of Rt. 578. Turn south on East Road and left on Houston. There is a call button at the gate. Call ahead if arriving after 6 p.m. Caution: Houston Avenue east from Rt. 19 comes to a dead end in a sand-pit.

THE ISLAND GROUP

22146 Dupree Drive
Land O'Lakes, FL 34639

FLORIDA

813/996-3289

FACILITIES

ACCOMMODATIONS

Wheelchair Access
■ Vacation Villas
Cabins
Rooms
■ Cable TV
In-room Telephone
Trailers
   heated
   w/bath
   cooking
Restaurant
Lounge
Snack Bar
Store

CAMPING

■ Tent Spaces
R/V Spaces
   w/elec
   w/water
   w/sewer
Disposal Station
■ Showers
   cold
   hot
Laundromat
■ Community Kitchen
■ Picnic Tables
■ Playground ("A" frame swing)
Pets/Leash only

RECREATION

■ Swimming Pool (45-foot)
■ Lake
■ Whirlpool/Spa
■ Sauna
■ Exercise Equipment
■ Tennis (Paddle)
■ Volleyball
■ Shuffleboard
■ Horseshoes
Petanque
Miniten
Badminton
■ Fishing
■ Recreation Hall
Children's Activities
Teen Activities

INFORMATION

Club Personality
The Island Group offers a secure, private, and hassle-free environment for naturists who want to get away from the restrictions and expense of large commercial organizations.
Mailing Address: P.O. Box 397 Land O'Lakes, FL 34639

Description of Grounds
Situated on a 3-acre island surrounded by water and trees for complete privacy, the club provides an excellent environment for the first timer.

Neighboring Sights and Attractions
The Island Group's facility is just 15 miles north of Tampa. Bush Gardens, Gulf beaches, golf courses, Adventure Island, and Disney World are all within easy driving distance.

Honored Discounts
Discounts on grounds fees for AANR members. Group rates are available.

Directions
The Island is located north of Tampa, Florida, off Highway 41 on Dupree Drive, about 4 miles north of Highway 54. Paradise Lakes and Lake Como are just south of this intersection.
Going north, take the first right after the Circle K; going south, take the first left after the post office. Keep to the left of fork and watch for The Island Group's sign.

55

LAKE COMO CLUB

**20500 Cot Road
Lutz, FL 33549**

FLORIDA

813/949-1810

FACILITIES

INFORMATION

ACCOMMODATIONS

- Wheelchair Access
- Vacation Villas
- ■ Cabins (1)
- ■ Rooms (20)
- Cable TV
- In-room Telephone
- ■ Trailers (1)
  - ● heated
  - ● w/bath
  - ● cooking
- ■ Restaurant
- ■ Lounge
- Snack Bar
- Store

CAMPING

- ■ Tent Spaces (15)
- ■ R/V Spaces (75)
  - ● w/elec (75)
  - ● w/water (75)
  - w/sewer
- ■ Disposal Station
- ■ Showers
  - ● cold (5)
  - ● hot (7)
- ■ Laundromat
- Community Kitchen
- ■ Picnic Tables (50)
- ■ Playground
- ■ Pets/Leash only

RECREATION

- ■ Swimming Pool (30'x40')
- ■ Lake (35-acre)
- ■ Whirlpool/Spa
- ■ Sauna
- Exercise Equipment
- ■ Tennis
- ■ Volleyball
- ■ Shuffleboard
- ■ Horseshoes
- ■ Petanque
- Badminton
- ■ Recreation Hall
- ■ Billiards
- ■ Ping Pong
- ■ Fishing
- ■ Boat Rentals
- ■ Children's/Teen Activities

■ ● denotes availability

Club Personality

Lake Como, Florida's original nude recreation community, has occupied the same beautiful 200-acre site in southern Pasco County since 1940. In addition to Lake Como's regular members, the club welcomes more than 20,000 day visitors and overnighters each year.
Fax: 813/949-4937

Description of Grounds

Lake Como operates a full service restaurant and two lounges. There is a large heated swimming pool, sauna, and 25-person hot tub. Sports facilities include tennis, volleyball, petanque, horseshoes, shuffleboard, billiards, and ping pong. The centerpiece of Lake Como's park-like setting is a 35-acre lake with a white sand beach.

Directions

One block south of S.R. 54 on HWY 41. West on Leonard Road; follow $^1/_2$ mile to Cot Road. Club entrance—orange grove on the left. Follow Cot Road to the office.

Lake

'A traditional **nudist** resort with a **family** atmosphere."

Neighboring Sights and Attractions
Twenty minutes from Tampa Airport; 30 minutes from Busch Gardens and Adventure Island; 40 minutes from Gulf Beaches, St. Pete and Clearwater; $1^{1}/_{2}$ hours from Disney and Sea World.

Honored Discounts
Discounts for AANR and TNS members. College-student discount with valid student I.D.

Como Club

RIVIERA NATURIST RESORT

P.O. Box 2233
Pace, FL 32572

FLORIDA

850/994-3665

FACILITIES

ACCOMMODATIONS

- ■ Wheelchair Access
  Vacation Villas
  Cabins
  Rooms
- ■ Cable TV
  In-room Telephone
- ■ Trailers (1)
  - ● heated
  - ● w/bath
  - ● cooking
  Restaurant
  Lounge
- ■ Snack Bar
  Store

CAMPING

- ■ Tent Spaces (8)
- ■ R/V Spaces (18)
  - ● w/elec (26)
  - ● w/water (26)
  - ● w/sewer (18)
- ■ Disposal Station
- ■ Showers
  - ● cold (4)
  - ● hot (4)
- ■ Laundromat
- ■ Community Kitchen
- ■ Picnic Tables (10)
  Playground
- ■ Pets/Leash only

RECREATION

- ■ Swimming Pool (20' x 40')
  Lake
- ■ Whirlpool/Spa
  Sauna
- ■ Covered Pavilion
  Tennis
- ■ Volleyball
  Shuffleboard
- ■ Horseshoes
  Petanque
  Miniten
  Badminton
  Fishing
- ■ Recreation Hall
- ■ Children's Activities
- ■ Teen Activities
- ■ One-Half Mile Jogging Track

■● denotes availability

INFORMATION

Club Personality
Riviera Naturist Resort's personality is summed up in three words: "Very friendly atmosphere."
Fax: 904/994-3624
Web Site: http://adpsercives.com/rr/

Description of Grounds
This family oriented park of 16 secluded acres is located in Florida's Panhandle, just north of the town of Pace. Eight acres are encircled by a nine-foot privacy fence, with shade trees for relaxing and large grassy areas for sunning.

Neighboring Sights and Attractions
The Aviation Museum is less than 25 miles away, and the beach is only 30 minutes away. Restaurants and grocery stores are within 4 miles, while entertainment shops and motels may be found within an 11-mile radius.

Honored Discounts
Twenty percent discount for AANR members. Ten percent for The Naturist Society and Good Sam.

Directions
Located north of Pace, Florida between Highway 197 and Highway 197A on Guernsey Road.

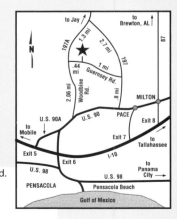

SEMINOLE HEALTH CLUB

3800 S.W. 142nd Avenue
Davie, FL 33330

FLORIDA

954/473-0231

FACILITIES

ACCOMMODATIONS

Wheelchair Access
Vacation Villas
■ Cabins (2)
■ Rooms (6)
■ Cable TV
In-room Telephone
Trailers
   heated
   w/bath
   cooking
Restaurant
Lounge
Snack Bar
Store

CAMPING

■ Tent Spaces (10)
■ R/V Spaces (50)
  ● w/elec (50)
  ● w/water (50)
   w/sewer
■ Disposal Station
■ Showers
  ● cold
  ● hot
■ Laundromat
  Community Kitchen
■ Picnic Tables
■ Playground
■ Pets/Leash only

RECREATION

■ Swimming Pool
■ Pond
■ Whirlpool/Spa
  Sauna
■ Exercise Equipment
■ Tennis
■ Volleyball
■ Shuffleboard
■ Horseshoes
■ Badminton
■ Petanque Courts (2)
■ Recreation Hall
■ Billiards
■ Bingo
■ Children/Teen Activities
■ Game Room
■ Table Tennis

INFORMATION

Club Personality
Seminole Health Club, an 11-acre park, is the southernmost landed club in the United States. It not only has many recreational activities of its own, but is situated in the center of a sightseeing paradise. Open all year.

Description of Grounds
Two cabins, six rooms, ten tent spaces, and 50 RV sites with water and electric hookups are available. Relax in the heated pool and whirlpool or join in club activities such as volleyball, table tennis, billiards and bingo.

Neighboring Sights and Attractions
Sailing, fishing, Everglades tours, Jai Alai, horse and dog tracks, an Indian village, alligator wrestling, air boats, cruises to the Bahamas, and Miami/Ft. Lauderdale nightlife.

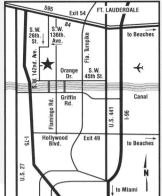

Directions
From the north: Take Sunshine Parkway to 595. West to Flamingo Road, south to Orange Drive, west to 142nd Avenue. Turn right, and Seminole is on right side of the road one-half mile.

SUNBURST RESORT

2375 Horn Road
Milton, FL 32570

FLORIDA

904/675-6807

FACILITIES

INFORMATION

A C C O M M O D A T I O N S

Wheelchair Access
Vacation Villas
■ Rental Units (7)
Rooms
■ Cable TV in Clubhouse
In-room Telephone
Trailers
   heated
   w/bath
   microwave
Restaurant
Lounge
■ Snack Bar (Weekends)
Store

C A M P I N G

■ Tent Spaces
■ R/V Spaces (12)
  ● w/elec
  ● w/water
  ● w/sewer
■ Disposal Station
■ Showers (2)
  ● cold
  ● hot
■ Laundromat
Community Kitchen
■ Picnic Tables (20)
Playground
■ Pets/Leash only

R E C R E A T I O N

■ Swiming Pool (2)
Lake
■ Whirlpool/Spa
Sauna
Exercise Equipment
■ Tennis
■ Volleyball (Sand and Water)
■ Shuffleboard
■ Horseshoes
Petanque
■ Billiards
Badminton
■ Ping Pong
Recreation Hall
Children's Activities
Teen Activities
■ Game Room

● denotes availability
■

Club Personality
Located in the rolling hills of the Florida Panhandle, Sunburst Resort is just 30 miles from Pensacola. Friendly and family oriented, the club is open year-round.

Description of Grounds
The resort sits on 20 acres of beautiful wooded land. Neat, clean, well maintained, and entirely fenced-in for privacy and security.

Directions
Sixteen miles north of Milton, Florida, just off Highway 87, turn left on County Road 178, go down the hill to first paved road, right, across wooden bridge to second left, look for Sunburst sign.

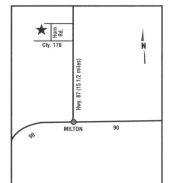

Sunb

"A private, comfortable family resort."

Neighboring Sights and Attractions

Beautiful white sandy beaches on the Gulf of Mexico are less than one hour away. Canoeing and fishing are nearby. Shops, restaurants, motels, and entertainment may be found within 15 miles. For the more adventurous, tube and canoe trips are five minutes from the club.

urst Resort

FLORIDA
561/468-8512

SUNNIER PALMS
8800 Okeechobee Road
Ft. Pierce, FL 34945

ACTIVITIES & RECREATION

Camping
RV Sites with Hookups
Swimming Pool (20' x 40')
Hot Tub (December '97)
Rental Rooms
Community Kitchen
Potlucks Every Sunday
Volleyball
Shuffleboard
Fishing
Children's Playground

Club Personality
Sunnier Palms is a not-for-profit cooperative nudist park operated entirely by member-volunteers. The club welcomes all nudists and naturists who wish to live in harmony with nature and one another. Visitors are always welcomed.
Fax: 561/468-9786

Description of Grounds
Sunnier Palms is located on 25 acres of beautiful subtropical land on Florida's Treasure Coast. The park includes a 12-acre wildlife forest with lovely well-kept trails, and a small pond. The grounds also contain citrus and litchi trees and a variety of flowering plants. Restaurants and shops nearby; ocean beaches are just 10 miles away.

SANIBEL NATURISTS
P.O. Box 6789
Ft. Myers, FL 33911

FLORIDA
941/995-NUDE

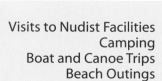

ACTIVITIES & RECREATION

Visits to Nudist Facilities
Camping
Boat and Canoe Trips
Beach Outings
Picnics
Pool and Volleyball Parties

General Information
Sanibel Naturists is a nonlanded family oriented club covering the west coast of Florida from Sarasota southward. Frequent activities are held year-round. The club's goal is to preserve and expand opportunities for clothing-optional recreational activities and to promote their legal and public acceptance. Singles, couples and families are welcome.

SUNNY SANDS RESORT

502 Central Blvd.
Pierson, FL 32180-2323

FLORIDA

904/749-2233

FACILITIES

ACCOMMODATIONS

- Wheelchair Access
- ■ Vacation Villas
- Cabins
- Rooms
- ■ Cable TV
- In-room Telephone
- Trailers
  - heated
  - w/bath
  - cooking
- Restaurant
- Lounge
- ■ Snack Bar
- Store
- ■ Poolside Bar

CAMPING

- ■ Tent Spaces (40)
- ■ R/V Spaces (14)
  - ● w/elec (2)
  - ● w/water (2)
  - ● w/sewer (12)
- ■ Disposal Station
- ■ Showers
  - ● cold (2)
  - ● hot (3)
- ■ Laundromat
- Community Kitchen
- ■ Picnic Tables (14)
- Playground
- ■ Pets/Leash only

RECREATION

- ■ Swimming Pool (20'x40')
- Lake
- ■ Whirlpool/Spa
- Sauna
- Exercise Equipment
- ■ Basketball
- ■ Volleyball
- ■ Shuffleboard
- ■ Horseshoes
- ■ Petanque
- ■ Billiards
- ■ Badminton
- ■ Fishing
- Recreation Hall
- Children's Activities
- Teen Activities
- ■ Ping Pong

■ ● denotes availability

INFORMATION

Club Personality
Sunny Sands radiates Southern hospitality at its best. Enjoy its laid-back lifestyle while relaxing under the trees, taking long walks, or playing a hustle-bustle game of volleyball. Leg's Bar is the social focal point where you can sip your favorite beverage or engage in a challenging game of cards. Open year-round.
Fax: 904/749-0240
Web Site: http://www.greyhawkes.com/sunnysands

Description of Grounds
Sunny Sands Resort's 50 acres of wide open grassy areas and heavily shaded oak groves are 20 miles north of Deland in central Florida. The club has a full range of activities and amenities, including a fishing-only lake.

Neighboring Sights and Attractions
Sunny Sands is an hour or less from Disney World, Universal Studios and Cape Canaveral. Closer to the club are the world famous Daytona Beach and Daytona Speedway. Nearby is Ocala Forest and Blue Spring State Park. Cypress Cove Nudist Resort is less than 100 miles away.

Honored Discounts
Discounts for AANR, TNS and INF members.

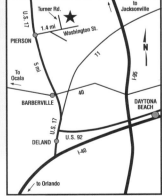

Directions
On Highway 17, 20 miles north of Deland, proceed east on Washington Street for $1\frac{1}{2}$ miles, then turn left on Turner Road for one-fourth mile to the entrance.

FLORIDA
941/643-3022

SOUTHERN EXPOSURE

P.O. Box 990192
Naples, FL 34116

ACTIVITIES & RECREATION

General Information
Southern Exposure, with over 250 members and still growing, is a club on the move and looking to make good things happen. Special events are listed in the club calendar.
Fax 941/643-3022
E-mail: Lockstock@AOL.com

Camping
Swimming in a Spring-Fed Lake
Monthly Social, and Cookout
Day Club

SOUTHWEST FLORIDA NATURISTS

FLORIDA

P.O. Box 3183
Ft. Myers, FL 33918-3183

ACTIVITIES & RECREATION

Bowling Get-togethers
Barbecues
Dinner, and Wine and Cheese
Parties
Swimming Socials

General Information
Southwest Florida Naturists is a family oriented, social nudist club. Membership is open to families and couples.

FACILITIES

ACCOMMODATIONS

- Wheelchair Access (limited)
- Vacation Villas
- Cabins
- Rooms
- Cable TV
- In-room Telephone
- Trailers (4)
  - heated
  - w/bath
  - cooking
- Restaurant
- Lounge
- Snack Bar
- Store
- Other

CAMPING

- Tent Spaces (50)
- R/V Spaces (48)
  - w/elec (48)
  - w/water (48)
  - w/sewer (40)
- Disposal Stations (2)
- Showers
  - cold (3)
  - hot (7)
- Laundromat
- Community Kitchen
- Picnic Tables
- Playground
- Pets/Leash only

RECREATION

- Swimming Pool (30,000 gallon)
- Lake
- Whirlpool/Spa
- Sauna
- Exercise Equipment
- Tennis
- Volleyball
- Shuffleboard
- Horseshoes
- Petanque
- Miniten
- Badminton
- Fishing
- Recreation Hall
- Club House
- Teen Activities
- Children's Activities

■ denotes availability

INFORMATION

Club Personality
For over 30 years Sunsport Gardens has provided family nudists with a warm and friendly environment. The club's diverse membership makes everyone—families, couples, singles and children—feel welcome.
Toll Free: 800/551-7217
Web site: http://www.sunsportgardens.com

Description of Grounds
Nearly 50 acres of beautiful, natural, sun-kissed southeastern Florida. All campsites provide a balance of sun and shade.

Neighboring Sights and Attractions
The club is located near the Atlantic Beaches—including world famous Palm Beach—and the Florida Everglades. An easy drive to both Disney World and the Florida Keys.

Honored Discounts
Discounts for AANR, TNS, Canadian Naturists and INF members.

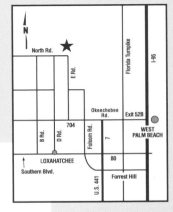

Directions
From the Florida Turnpike Exit 99, or I-95 exit 52B, go west to "D" Road. Turn right and continue to a dead end on North Road. Turn right. The entrance is one-quarter mile on the left.

FLORIDA

850/847-8537

TALLAHASSEE BARE-DEVILS

P.O. Box 6866
Tallahassee, FL 32314

 ACTIVITIES & RECREATION

General Information
Free in mind and body, at one with nature, this group rents 40 acres of unspoiled woodland with a beautiful swimming lake available for quiet relaxation every weekend year-round. Ethnically diverse members, largely young professionals run the club by consensus. The club maintains an active calendar of fully nude activities on public and private land, while educating all in naturist philosophy. Membership is made affordable for college students, singles, and especially families with children.
E-mail: tlhbared@freenet.scri.fsu.edu

Swimming and Sunbathing
Picnics and Campouts
Labeled Nature Trail
Full-Moon Skinnydips
Canoe, Beach and
Sinkhole Trips
Political Awareness

Special Events
College Greek Athletic Meet
Camp Tallasun for Children Ages 11-17

BARE BUDDIES

P.O. Box 81606
Atlanta, GA 30366

GEORGIA

404/264-6255

ACTIVITIES & RECREATION

Trips
Camping
Hot Tub Parties
Potluck/Dinner Parties
Hiking
Rafting

General Information
Bare Buddies is a club for all nudists—singles and couples. Bare Buddies' purpose is to create a family of friends who enjoy participating in nude social and recreational activities. The club schedules activities for its members throughout the year, hence, their motto: We never hibernate. Bare Buddies is affiliated with the American Association for Nude Recreation.
Web Site: http://www.cybernude.com/clubs/bareb/

Special Events
Annual Barbecue
Call for Information on Other Special Events

BELL ACRES RECREATION ENTERPRISE

GEORGIA

P.O. Box 302
Maysville, GA 30558

706/677-2931

FACILITIES

INFORMATION

ACCOMMODATIONS

- Wheelchair Access
- Vacation Villas
- ■ Cabins (4)
- Rooms
- Cable TV
- In-room Telephone
- Trailers
    - heated
    - w/bath
    - cooking
- Restaurant
- Lounge
- ■ Snack Bar
- ■ Store

CAMPING

- ■ Tent Spaces (15)
- ■ R/V Spaces (10)
    - ● w/elec (10)
    - ● w/water (10)
    - ● w/sewer (8)
- ■ Disposal Station
- ■ Showers
    - cold
    - ● hot (11)
- ■ Laundromat
- ■ Community Kitchen
- ■ Picnic Tables (8)
- ■ Playground ("A" frame swing)
- Pets/Leash only

RECREATION

- ■ Swimming Pool (60' x 30')
- Lake
- ■ Whirlpool/Spa
- Sauna
- ■ Exercise Equipment
- Tennis
- ■ Volleyball
- Shuffleboard
- ■ Horseshoes
- ■ Recreation Hall
- ■ Billiards
- ■ Table Tennis
- ■ Fishing
- ■ Nature Trails
- ■ Children's Activities
- ■ Kid's Playroom
- ■ Teen Activities

● denotes availability

Club Personality
Small enough to be friendly and family oriented, yet large enough to have excellent facilities, BARE has a rustic atmosphere with thoroughly modern conveniences. Members and guests take pride in making newcomers welcome.
Toll Free: 800/432-1436 Fax: 706/677-2847
Web site: http://www.cybernude.com/parks/bell/

Description of Grounds
Carved from 70 acres of hilly woodlands in northeast Georgia, Bell Acres opened in 1989. Wooded surroundings add special charm each season for a large swimming pool with its bathhouse, and for the clubhouse with its sun deck and hot tub. Campsites line two roads which lead to the hilltop home of the camp owners.

Neighboring Sights and Attractions
In the nearby Smoky Mountains are scenic trails, including the Appalachian, white water rafting, and a quaint Alpine village. BARE is four miles from large outlet malls and I-85 to Atlanta which is 70 miles away.

Honored Discounts
Twenty percent off grounds fees for INF, AANR and TNS members.

Directions
From Interstate 85 Exit 53 (U.S. 441) go north toward Homer. One mile from interchange cross the Grove River and turn left off U.S. 441 on the next paved road; McDonald Circle. Go 1.7 miles—beware a dangerous curve—to a dirt road on the left, Hembree Road. Go 0.6 miles on the dirt road to Bell Acres Road on the right where there is a cement block house. Follow Bell Acres Road to club entrance.

GEORGIA
706/265-6110

HIDDEN VALLEY
49 Valley Drive
Dawsonville, GA 30534

ACCOMMODATIONS & RECREATION

Club Personality
Hidden Valley, a 110-acre planned resort in the foothills of the north Georgia mountains, is a peaceful setting for family fun.
http://www.cybernude.com/HiddenValley/

Description of Grounds
At Hidden Valley, a sunny meadow nestled in the center of the property is bordered by two streams and a dense forest.

Neighboring Sights and Attractions
Within a short drive are the Alpine Village, Helen, several beautiful hiking trails, the gold-panning town of Dahlonega, Dawsonville's premier outlet mall with over 70 stores, and Lake Lanier.

RV Spaces with Full Hookups
Rental Rooms
Restaurant and Snack Bar
Swimming Pool
Pond
Whirlpool/Spa
Tennis
Volleyball
Recreation Hall
Playground

SANS TRAVEL CLUB
P.O. Box 770
Lawrenceville, GA 30046

GEORGIA
770/962-2236

ACTIVITIES & RECREATION

Events (SANSSPOTS) at Local Clubs
Hot Tub and Covered Dish Dinners in town
Road Trips to Regional Clubs

General Information
Join, and be a part of it all.

SANS is an extended family of kindred souls who share a common interest in social nude recreation. Old and new friends gathering together for one purpose: to have fun and enjoy life ... *naturally*!

Visit SANS' Web Site:
http://www.randomc.com/ESA/sans.shtml

MOUNTAIN CREEK GROVE

258 Grove Lane
Cleveland, GA 30528

GEORGIA
800/863-NUDE

FACILITIES

ACCOMMODATIONS

- ■ Wheelchair Access
- Vacation Villas
- Cabins
- ■ Rooms (3)
- Cable TV
- In-room Telephone
- Trailers
  - heated
  - w/bath
  - cooking
- Restaurant
- Lounge
- ■ Snack Bar
- Store

CAMPING

- ■ Tent Spaces (20)
- ■ R/V Spaces (16)
  - ● w/elec (16)
  - ● w/water (16)
  - w/sewer
- ■ Disposal Station
- ■ Showers
  - ● cold (1)
  - ● hot (4)
- ■ Laundromat
- Community Kitchen
- ■ Picnic Tables (12)
- ■ Playground
- ■ Pets/Leash only

RECREATION

- ■ Swimming Pool (20' x 40')
- Lake
- ■ Whirlpool/Spa
- Sauna
- ■ Exercise Equipment
- Tennis
- ■ Volleyball
- ■ Shuffleboard
- ■ Horseshoes
- ■ Recreation Hall
- ■ Table Tennis
- ■ Darts
- ■ Billiards
- ■ Fishing
- ■ Badminton
- Children's Activities
- ■ Teen Activities

■ ● denotes availability

INFORMATION

Club Personality
A place where people visit and friends stay. A family oriented nudist resort with some of the friendliest folks in the South. Permanent and part-time residents from all walks of life make visitors feel welcome.
Phone: 706/865-6930   Fax: 706/865-5521
E-mail: mtncreek@stc.net

Description of Grounds
The natural beauty of the club's seventy-seven wooded acres in the north Georgia mountains is beyond description. Enjoy the ripple of Blue Creek along with nature's other sounds in the quiet morning and evening hours. Take a peaceful stroll, sit by the creek, or join in the fun and games.

Neighboring Sights and Attractions
The Alpine Village of Helen and historic Clarkesville are nearby, with restaurants, motels, antique shops and art galleries scattered throughout the area. Golf courses, fishing streams, tubing facilities, water falls and hiking trails are nearby.

Honored Discounts
Discounts to AANR, INF and TNS members. Call for membership requirement and weekly specials.

Directions
From Interstate 85, follow the map to Highway 384/Duncan Bridge Road. Go 10 miles on 384 to Stovall Road. Turn right on Stovall Road. Proceed 0.7 miles to Cedar Hollow Road and turn right. Go straight off Cedar Hollow Road onto Grove Lane at the Mountain Creek Grove sign. Proceed to electronic gate and call from phone booth for entrance.

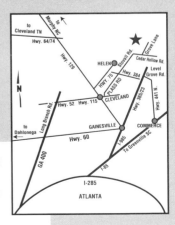

SERENDIPITY PARK

95 Cedar Hollow Road
Cleveland, GA 30528

GEORGIA

706/219-3993

FACILITIES

ACCOMMODATIONS

- Wheelchair Access
  Vacation Villas
- Cabins (2)
  Rooms
  Cable TV
  In-room Telephone
- Trailers (2)/Park Models (3)
  - heated
  - w/bath
  - cooking
- Restaurant
  Lounge
  Snack Bar
- Store

CAMPING

- Tent Spaces (30)
- R/V Spaces (35)
  - w/elec (35)
  - w/water (35)
  - w/sewer (35)
- Disposal Station
- Showers
  - cold (6)
  - hot (6)
  Laundromat
  Community Kitchen
- Picnic Tables (15)
- Playground
- Pets/Leash only

RECREATION

- Heated Swimming Pool
  Lake
- Whirlpool/Spa
- Sauna
- Exercise Equipment
- Water Volleyball
- Volleyball
- Hiking
- Horseshoes
- Petanque
- Recreation Hall
- Large Screen TV Area
- Billiards
- Table Tennis
- Tanning Beds
- Dance Floor
- Children's Activities

■ denotes availability

INFORMATION

Club Personality

Serendipity Park is a family nudist resort where children are welcome and a friendly atmosphere prevails. Open all year, there are ongoing activities for all seasons.
Toll Free: 888/NUDE-ONE
Web site: http://www.cybernude.com/resorts/serend/

Description of Grounds

The pool and clubhouse complex is on a flat area surrounded by wildlife, wild flowers, sauna, fauna, rolling hills, woodlands with many varieties of trees, springs, Blue Creek, and a view of Blue Ridge Mountains.

Neighboring Sights and Attractions

Within reasonable driving distance are the Alpine Village of Helen, many gold panning sites, Babyland General Hospital—home of the Cabbage Patch Kids—hiking trails, white water rafting, county fairs and markets, beautiful north Georgia mountains, waterfalls and much more. Near motels, restaurants and specialty foods.

Honored Discounts

Discounts to AANR, TNS, ANSP, and INF members.

Directions

From the Cleveland Square Hwy 15 east 3.8 miles. Left onto Pless Road. 1.7 miles on Pless to stop sign. Cross over to Stovall Road, a gravel road. $1/2$ miles to Cedar Hollow Road. Turn right, one block to entrance for RVs. Autos can continue on Stovall to entrance on right.

KONA SUN CLUB

P.O. Box 390304
Kailua-Kona, HI 96740

HAWAII

808/326-2752

ACTIVITIES & RECREATION

Nude Beach Gatherings
Pool parties at Members' Homes
Government Relations

General Information

The Kona Sun Klub was established to provide an organized basis for dealing with government officials with the goal of keeping Honokohau Beach open for nude use. The club is also prepared to offer free trip-planning assistance to nudist travelers, including beach information and clothing optional lodging alternatives. The club is presently seeking grounds for a future nudist resort.
Fax: 808/326-2752
E-mail: Konasun@gte.net

IDAHO

208/882-0364

General Information

Running Bares, a nonlanded AANR club, is a group of folks looking for relaxation while enjoying a clothes-free lifestyle.
E-mail: MIKEF@UIDAHO.EDU

RUNNING BEARS

P.O. Box 9714
Moscow, ID 83843

ACTIVITIES & RECREATION

Hot Tub Parties
Winter Indoor Swims
Hot Spring Trips
Theme Potlucks
Travel to Landed Clubs

BARE BACKERS

P.O. Box 5781
Boise, ID 83705

IDAHO

208/322-6853

FACILITIES

ACCOMMODATIONS

Wheelchair Access
Vacation Villas
Cabins
Rooms
Cable TV
In-room Telephone
Trailers
  heated
  w/bath
  cooking
Restaurant
Lounge
Snack Bar
Store

CAMPING

- Tent Spaces (4)
- R/V Spaces (6)
  - ● w/elec
  - ● w/water
  - w/sewer
  Disposal Station
- Showers
  - ● cold
  - ● hot
  Laundromat
  Community Kitchen
- Picnic Tables (6)
- Playground
- Pets/Leash only

RECREATION

- Swimming Pool (4' x 24')
  Lake
  Whirlpool/Spa
  Sauna
  Exercise Equipment
  Tennis
- Volleyball
  Shuffleboard
- Horseshoes
  Petanque
  Miniten
- Hiking Trails
  Fishing
  Recreation Hall
- Children's Activities
- Teen Activities

■ denotes availability

INFORMATION

Club Personality
Home to the Bare Backers is Bare Mountain Hideaway, phone 208/345-8998. Members enjoy hiking, volleyball, swimming, and lounging on the lawn with friends. Bare Mountain is open from May to October, with summer temperatures of 80 to 100 degrees and very little humidity. Temperatures at night run in the comfortable 50 to 60 degrees range.

Description of Grounds
Bare Mountain is an old gold-mining camp situated on 130 acres of hillside and many miles of trails. The club is very primitive with no drinking water and no sewage system, yet it does have a glorious scenic valley lined with pine trees and wildflowers. There are 40 permanent sites for campers and RVs which are rented to members and visitors. Most sites have running water.

Neighboring Sights and Attractions
Lucky Peak reservoir, with great fishing and water skiing, is less than five miles away. Idaho City, an attractive, historic mining community, is nearby, and Boise, the state capital, has many fine attractions, activities, and restaurants.

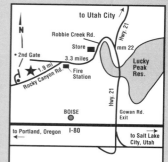

Directions
Take Highway 21 north out of Boise for 21 miles. Turn left at Mile Marker 22 onto Robbie Creek Road. Go 3.3 miles and turn left at the fire house, Mile Marker 261 onto Rocky Canyon Road. Go 1.9 miles, turn right at second gate (look for Bare Backers' mailbox).

FACILITIES

INFORMATION

ACCOMMODATIONS

Wheelchair Access
Vacation Villas
Cabins
■ Rooms (3)
Cable TV
In-room Telephone
Trailers
  heated
  w/bath
  cooking
■ Restaurant
Lounge
Snack Bar
Store

CAMPING

■ Tent Spaces (10)
■ R/V Spaces (20)
  ● w/elec
  ● w/water
    w/sewer
■ Disposal Station
■ Showers
  ● cold
  ● hot
Laundromat
Community Kitchen
■ Picnic Tables
■ Playground
■ Pets/Leash only

RECREATION

Swimming Pool
■ Pond
■ Whirlpool/Spa
Sauna
Exercise Equipment
Tennis
■ Volleyball
■ Shuffleboard
■ Horseshoes
■ Bocce Ball
Miniten
Badminton
■ Fishing
■ Recreation Hall
■ Calandar of Events
■ Teen Activities

Club Personality
Open from May 1 to October 1, Blue Lake Club is a friendly, family oriented resort. Pets on a leash are welcome at the campsite.

Description of Grounds
Located in the beautiful Rock River Valley of northwestern Illinois, this 20-acre park is nestled into a natural terrain of sunny and shaded areas. The grounds, which are inspected annually by the state of Illinois, are always neat and clean.

Neighboring Sights and Attractions
The club is 30 miles east of Moline, Rock Island and Davenport, which border the Mississippi River. There is boating on the river, plus many other attractions for individual interests.

Honored Discounts
Discounts for AANR and The Naturist Society members.

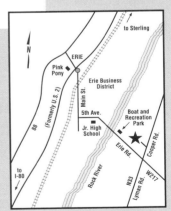

Directions
Exit from Interstate 80 (Illinois) onto Interstate 88 eastbound. Follow I-88 approximately 18 miles to the Erie-Albany exit. Follow access road two miles into Erie to the first stop sign, turn right onto Illinois Route 2, for three blocks. Turn left at the Pink Pony Drive-in onto 6th Avenue for one block, turn right onto 5th Avenue, turn left, go three miles to Cooper Road, turn left to the first drive, turn left into lane.

CHICAGO SUN CLUBS

ILLINOIS

P.O. Box 8135
Cicero, IL 60804

630/243-9614

INFORMATION

General Information

A year-round, clothing-optional, nonlanded Chicago-based group. During the summer months Chicago Sun Clubs sponsor weekend trips to many nudist parks and beaches. During the winter months, a variety of clothing-optional activities are held at rented indoor sports centers and recreation complexes rented especially for the clubs' private use, or at members' homes. For more information send a stamped, self-addressed envelope and $2 to the club.

WINTER ACTIVITIES & RECREATION

- Walleyball Tournaments
- Buff Bowling
- Health Club Parties
- Hot Tubbing
- Indoor Swim/Splash Parties
- Get-Away Weekends
- Cookouts
- Potluck Dinners
- Wacky Nude Olympics

CHICAGO SUN CLUBS

P.O. Box 8135
Cicero, IL 60804

ILLINOIS

630/243-9614

SUMMER ACTIVITIES & RECREATION

- Weekend Camping Trips
- Beach Parties
- Canuding
- Volleyball Tournaments
- Picnics and Barbecue Cookouts
- Swimming, Sunning
- Boating and Fishing
- Hiking
- Nude Regional and National Conventions
- Other Outdoor Activities

Special Events
Theme Parties, including:
Halloween, Mardi Gras,
Las Vegas Nite,
Nude New Year's Eve,
Roman Toga Nite,
Hawaiian Luau

ILLINOIS

314/898-3190

ILLI MO UTOPIANS

P.O. Box 92
Wood River, IL 62095

ACTIVITIES & RECREATION

General Information
The Illi Mo Utopians is a family oriented travel club founded in 1989 for the purpose of enjoying the nudist lifestyle. Members subscribe to the AANR philosophy that natural exposure to the sun and air promotes health, happiness and a sense of well-being in both mind and body. Write to the club for more information.

Visiting Landed Clubs
Sports
Picnicking
Camping
Hot Tubbing
Relaxing

FERN HILLS CLUB

7330 South Rockport Road
Bloomington, IN 47403

INDIANA

812/824-4489

FACILITIES

ACCOMMODATIONS

Wheelchair Access
Vacation Villas
Cabins
■ Rooms (5)
Cable TV
In-room Telephone
■ Trailers (7)
● heated
● w/bath
● cooking
■ Restaurant
Lounge
Snack Bar
Store

CAMPING

■ Tent Spaces
■ R/V Spaces (18)
● w/elec
● w/water
● w/sewer
■ Disposal Station
■ Showers (8)
● cold
● hot
Laundromat
Community Kitchen
Picnic Tables
■ Playground
Pets/Leash only

RECREATION

■ Swimming Pool
Lake
■ Whirlpool/Spa
■ Sauna
Exercise Equipment
Tennis
■ Volleyball
■ Shuffleboard
Horseshoes
Petanque
Miniten
Badminton
Fishing
■ Recreation Hall
Children's Activities
Teen Activities

■ ● denotes availability

INFORMATION

Club Personality
Open May through October, this 74-acre park in southern Indiana has many green, grassy areas for sunbathing. Guests may enjoy a potluck dinner on the third Sunday of each month from November through April.

Description of Grounds
Five rooms and seven rental trailers are provided for guests. Unlimited tent spaces and 18 RV sites with water, electric and sewer hookups are available. A disposal station, eight showers, a restaurant and playground are all conveniently located.

Neighboring Sights and Attractions
Shops, restaurants, motels, churches and entertainment may be found at Bloomington, just seven miles to the southwest.

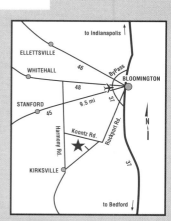

Directions
Coming from the south, take 37 Bypass to Rockport Road. Go left four miles. Look for "Ripple" on mailbox. The driveway is on the right.

FT. WAYNE NATURISTS

INDIANA

P.O. Box 12615
Fort Wayne, IN 46864

ACTIVITIES & RECREATION

Monthly Parties
Visits to Landed Clubs

Special Events
Annual Houseboat Trip
New Year's Party

General Information

The Fort Wayne Naturists is a family oriented travel club now in its 12th year. Members hold year-round monthly activities, including off-season indoor activity, theme parties and dances, potlucks, hot tub parties, and lake picnics.

INDIANA

219/462-6643

LAKE O'THE WOODS CLUB

P.O. Box 53
Valparaiso, IN 46384

Club Personality

This cooperative member-owned club offers opportunities for both quiet relaxation and friendly socialization. The club is open year-round, with many amenities including two fireplaces, a sauna, and heated swimming pool and a hot tub to ward off those winter chills.
Fax: 630/377-9914

Description of Grounds

A beautiful 26-acre lake offers fishing, boating and swimming in the summer, and ice-fishing, sledding and skating in the winter. The clubhouse is the center of social events and informal gatherings. There are tent and RV sites, and sleeping rooms in the club lodge.

 ## ACCOMMODATIONS & RECREATION

Heated Swimming Pool
Whirlpool/Spa
Sauna
Rental Rooms
RV Spaces with Electric Hookup
Tennis
Volleyball
Shuffleboard
Horseshoes
Recreation Hall
Community Kitchen
Playground

SUNNY HAVEN

11425 Anderson Road
Granger, IN 46530

INDIANA

219/277-5356

FACILITIES

ACCOMMODATIONS

- ■ Wheelchair Access
- Vacation Villas
- ■ Cabins (6)
- Rooms
- Cable TV
- In-room Telephone
- Trailers
  - heated
  - w/bath
  - cooking
- Restaurant
- Lounge
- ■ Snack Bar
- ■ Store

CAMPING

- ■ Tent Spaces (20)
- ■ R/V Spaces (120)
  - ● w/elec (120)
  - ● w/water (120)
  - w/sewer
- ■ Disposal Station
- ■ Showers
  - ● cold (1)
  - ● hot (9)
- Laundromat
- Community Kitchen
- ■ Picnic Tables (16)
- ■ Playground
- ■ Pets/Leash only

RECREATION

- ■ Swimming Pool (24' x 50')
- Lake
- ■ Whirlpool/Spa
- ■ Sauna
- Exercise Equipment
- Tennis
- ■ Volleyball
- ■ Shuffleboard
- ■ Horseshoes
- Petanque
- ■ Miniten
- Badminton
- Fishing
- ■ Recreation Hall
- ■ Children's Activities
- Teen Activities
- ■ Nature Trail

■ = denotes availability

INFORMATION

Club Personality
Sunny Haven Recreation Park is one of the finest and friendliest family nudist parks in the Midwest. A cooperative club since 1947, it offers modern facilities at reasonable cost.
Mailing Address: P.O. Box 100-G, Granger, IN 46530

Description of Grounds
Sunny Haven offers 120 level campsites with sandy soil, some wooded and some grassy. The social and recreational centerpiece of the club is a 24-foot-by-50-foot heated pool. Adjacent are a sauna, spa, and large deck for sunning and relaxing. Nearby are three miniten courts, two shuffleboard courts, horseshoe pits, volleyball courts, a snack bar, and a clubhouse.

Neighboring Sights and Attractions
South Bend, 10 miles away, has the University of Notre Dame and the College Football Hall of Fame. Elkhart has RV factory tours. Nappanee and Shipshewana have famous Amish restaurants, crafts, auctions, and flea markets.

Honored Discounts
Discounts to AANR, INF, NNC, and TNS members.

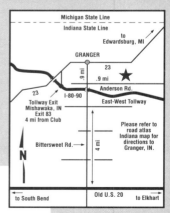

Directions
From I-80/90 take Exit 83. Right on Capital Avenue to State Road 23. Right on State Road 23 to Bittersweet Road. Right on Bittersweet Road to Anderson Road. Left on Anderson Road to Sunny Haven sign. Left on gravel drive to gate.

SUNSHOWER

3263 Mattie Harris Road
Centerville, IN 47330

INDIANA

765/855-2785

FACILITIES

ACCOMMODATIONS

- Wheelchair Access
  Vacation Villas
- Cabins (1)
  Rooms
  Cable TV
  In-room Telephone
- Trailers (1)
  - heated
  - w/bath
  - cooking
  Restaurant
  Lounge
  Snack Bar
  Store
- Ice and Soda

CAMPING

- Tent Spaces (100)
- R/V Spaces (30)
  - w/elec (30)
  - w/water (30)
  - w/sewer (3)
  Disposal Station
- Showers
  cold
  - hot (5)
  Laundromat
- Community Kitchen
- Picnic Tables (18)
- Playground
- Pets/Leash only

RECREATION

- Swimming Pool (50' x 90')
  Lake
- Whirlpool/Spa
  Sauna
  Exercise Equipment
  Tennis
  Volleyball
- Shuffleboard
- Horseshoes
  Petanque
- Miniten
- Badminton
  Fishing
- Recreation Hall
- Children's Activities
  Teen Activities
- Hiking Trails

INFORMATION

Club Personality
A family oriented camp, Sunshower Country Club offers a variety of weekend activities from mid-May through mid-September. Guests are invited to relax on the beautiful grounds, or to join in one of the friendly sports activities where newcomers are always welcome. Mailing Address: P.O. Box 33487, Cleveland, OH 44133

Description of Grounds
Sunshower Country Club is located on 98 acres of rolling grass and forest reserve land. The L-shaped pool—largest in the MSA—is surrounded by a concrete sunning area with a hot tub and umbrella-covered tables nearby.

Neighboring Sights and Attractions
Located in historical Centerville, Indiana, the antique capital of the world. Only 45 minutes from Wright Patterson Air Force Museum or two hours from King's Island. Groceries, supplies, motels and restaurants are within three miles.

Honored Discounts
Discounts to AANR, AARP and The Naturist Society members. Call in advance for rates and reservations.

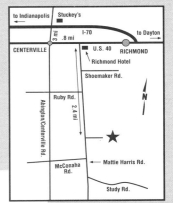

Directions
In Centerville, drive south on Mattie Harris (Corner of Mattie Harris Road and U.S. Highway 40) for 2.4 miles. Take the 6th drive on the left beyond Ruby Road. Look for a wide entrance with a green address sign that reads 3263.

79

TRI-STATE COUNTRY CLUB

79 Drakes Ridge
Bennington, IN 47011

INDIANA

812/427-3914

FACILITIES

ACCOMMODATIONS

- Wheelchair Access
  Vacation Villas
  Cabins
- Rooms (1)
  Cable TV
  In-room Telephone
- Trailers—Pop-up (2)
    heated
    w/bath
    ● cooking (1)
  Restaurant
  Lounge
- Snack Bar
- Store (Limited Items)

CAMPING

- Tent Spaces (10)
- R/V Spaces—Small (2)
    ● w/elec (1)
    w/water
    w/sewer
- Disposal Station
- Showers
    cold
    ● hot (4)
  Laundromat
- Community Kitchen
- Picnic Tables (7)
- Playground
- Pets/Leash only (At Campsite)

RECREATION

- Swimming Pool (24' Diameter)
  Lake
  Whirlpool/Spa
  Sauna
- Hiking
  Tennis
- Volleyball
- Shuffleboard
  Horseshoes
  Petanque
  Miniten
- Library
- Table Tennis
- Badminton
- Recreation Hall
- Children's Activities

■ ● denotes availability

INFORMATION

Club Personality
Scenic, quiet, back to nature atmosphere where friendly members are involved in planning activities and operating the campground. The season is Memorial Day weekend through Labor Day weekend.

Description of Grounds
While the wooded grounds lend themselves to quiet camping, there are also hiking trails, fun and games, a clubhouse and activities for the children. With these options, guests choose for themselves whether to relax or to participate in the many activities centered around the swimming pool and sunning area.

Neighboring Sights and Attractions
Swiss Wine Festival in August. Paradise Gardens 50 miles. Cedar Trails and Sunshower approximately 100 miles. Three state parks nearby.

Honored Discounts
Discounts to AANR, INF and TNS members.

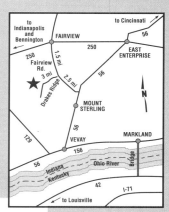

Directions
The mileage indicated on the map is the best aid in locating the club. Silver triangles are on posts at Route 56 turnoff (Fairview Road) and Drakes Ridge. Drakes Ridge turns off Fairview Road. Interstate 71 in northern Kentucky is the nearest freeway route between Louisville and the northern Kentucky-Cincinnati area and parallels U.S. 42.

CAMELOT

IOWA

P.O. Box 4753
Des Moines, IA 50306

ACTIVITIES & RECREATION

Potlucks and Picnics
Visits to Landed Nudist
Facilities
Social Gatherings
Swimming and Hot Tub
Parties

General Information
Serving the eastern two-thirds of Iowa, Camelot travel club provides social and recreational activities at members' homes and more distant parks and resorts. Membership is primarily couples and families. Camelot is proud to be the largest and oldest AANR charter club in Iowa.

IOWA

P.O. Box 34
Estherville, IA 51334-0034

DAKOTA PRAIRE SUN CLUB

ACTIVITIES & RECREATION

General Information
The Dakota Prairie Sun Club serves nudists in northwest Iowa, southwest Minnesota, southeast South Dakota and northeast Nebraska. In addition to their outdoor activities, members meet year-round in homes and rented spa facilities. A family oriented nonlanded club, welcoming inquiries from families, couples and singles. Write for more information.

Potlucks
Picnics
Saunas and Hot Tubbing
Theme Parties
Visits to Nudist Resorts
Visits to Parks and Beaches

Special Events
National Nude Weekend Trip
Annual Wine and Cheese Party
Annual Chili Feed

PRAIRIE HAVEN

19289 S. Morril Road
Scranton, KS 66537

KANSAS

785/793-2738

FACILITIES

ACCOMMODATIONS

Wheelchair Access
Vacation Villas
■ Cabins (2)
Rooms
Cable TV
In-room Telephone
■ Trailers (3)
    heated
    w/bath
    cooking
Restaurant
Lounge
Snack Bar
Store

CAMPING

■ Tent Spaces (34)
■ R/V Spaces (15)
    ● w/elec
    ● w/water
    ● w/sewer
■ Disposal Station
■ Showers
    cold
    hot
Laundromat
■ Community Kitchen
■ Picnic Tables (15)
■ Playground
Pets/Leash only

RECREATION

■ Swimming Pool
Lake
■ Whirlpool/Spa
Sauna
Exercise Equipment
■ Tennis
■ Volleyball
■ Shuffleboard
■ Horseshoes
Petanque
Miniten
Badminton
Fishing
■ Recreation Hall
Children's Activities
Teen Activities

■ ● denotes availability

INFORMATION

Club Personality
From April through October, Prairie Haven guests enjoy a delightful pool, an eight-foot hot tub in an enclosed gazebo, and two large sunning decks.

Description of Grounds
Located 23 miles south of Topeka, Kansas, the club is comprised of 30 acres of shaded park sites with modern facilities and maintained roads. Two cabins and three trailers are provided for guests. There are 34 tent spaces and 15 RV sites.

Neighboring Sights and Attractions
Shops and restaurants are found within seven miles of the club. Entertainment is only 10 miles away, while motels may be found 23 miles away.

Directions
Easy access for travelers from either Interstate 70 or Interstate 35 for campers and RVs. See map for directions or call during daytime hours.

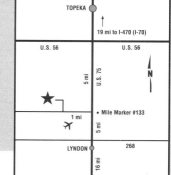

SANDY LANE CLUB

KANSAS

P.O. Box 1866
Hutchinson, KS 67504

316/543-2645

FACILITIES

ACCOMMODATIONS

- ■ Wheelchair Access
- Vacation Villas
- ■ Cabins (2)
- Rooms
- Cable TV
- In-room Telephone
- Trailers
  - heated
  - w/bath
  - cooking
- Restaurant
- Lounge
- ■ Snack Bar
- Store

CAMPING

- ■ Tent Spaces (5)
- ■ R/V Spaces (3)
  - ● w/elec
  - ● w/water
  - w/sewer
- ■ Disposal Station
- ■ Showers
  - ● cold (3)
  - ● hot (3)
  - Laundromat
- ■ Community Kitchen
- ■ Picnic Tables
- ■ Playground
- ■ Pets/Leash only

RECREATION

- ■ Swimming Pool (27' x 27')
- Lake
- ■ Whirlpool/Spa
- Sauna
- ■ Exercise Equipment
- Tennis
- ■ Volleyball
- ■ Shuffleboard
- Horseshoes
- Petanque
- Miniten
- Badminton
- Fishing
- Recreation Hall
- Children's Activities
- Teen Activities

INFORMATION

Club Personality
The Sandy Lane Club is proud of its clean air, good water and friendly atmosphere. A laid-back group in a country setting.

Description of Grounds
This 40-acre park is not really sandy, but a luxurious grassy area dotted with shade trees and completely enclosed by a catalpa tree grove.

Neighboring Sights and Attractions
Close to Kansas State Fairgrounds, shopping mall, and many dining establishments.

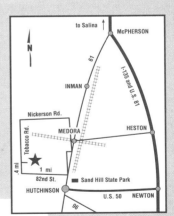

Directions
Travel 4.6 miles north of 30th Street on Highway 61. Turn west on 82nd Street for 1.0 miles, then north 0.4 miles. Turn east to the red gate and blow horn for entry.

KANSAS

913/649-2560

HEARTLAND NATURISTS

P.O. Box 9103
Shawnee Mission, KS 66201

ACTIVITIES & RECREATION

General Information

Heartland Naturists, formerly Kansans for a Natural Society, serves the Kansas City/Topeka area. Members plan at least one activity per month, as a nonlanded club, usually more in the summertime. Activities are held mostly at members' homes. Several times a year nude swimming, bowling or skating at local facilities are offered.

Nude Roller Skating
Indoor Swimming Parties
Nude Bowling
Theme Parties
Summer Swimming/
Sunbathing Parties
Hot Tubbing
Nude Limousine Rides

Special Events

Christmas Party and Gift Exchange
Community Outreach Programs
Valentine's Party

KYANA NATURISTS

P.O. Box 3453
Louisville, KY 40201

KENTUCKY

812/427-3914

ACTIVITIES & RECREATION

Spa and Athletic Club Events in
Winter Months
Joint Activities with Tri-State
Country Club

General Information

Kyana Naturists was formed to provide local activity in the Louisville, Kentucky, area. This friendly nonlanded group makes guests feel welcome.

Special Events

Fun Fest

LA PINES RANCH

29414 Cyprian Drive
Lacombe, LA 70445

LOUISIANA

504/882-5662

FACILITIES

ACCOMMODATIONS

- ■ Wheelchair Access
- Vacation Villas
- Cabins
- Rooms
- ■ Cable TV
- In-room Telephone
- ■ Trailers (5)
  - ● heated
  - ● w/bath (3)
  - cooking
- ■ Restaurant
- ■ Lounge
- ■ Snack Bar
- Store

CAMPING

- ■ Tent Spaces
- ■ R/V Spaces (6)
  - ● w/elec
  - ● w/water
  - ● w/sewer
- ■ Disposal Station
- ■ Showers
  - ● cold (6)
  - ● hot (6)
- ■ Laundromat
- Community Kitchen
- ■ Picnic Tables (6)
- ■ Playground
- ■ Pets/Leash only

RECREATION

- ■ Swimming Pool (21' x 45')
- Lake
- ■ Whirlpool/Spa
- Sauna
- ■ Exercise Equipment
- Tennis
- ■ Volleyball
- ■ Shuffleboard
- ■ Horseshoes
- Petanque
- Miniten
- ■ Badminton
- ■ Fishing
- ■ Recreation Hall
- ■ TV Room
- Teen Activities
- Children's Activities

■ denotes availability

INFORMATION

Club Personality
Located just 45 miles from New Orleans, this 10-acre park is open year-round. Facilities include swimming pool, whirlpool, volleyball, badminton, shuffleboard, horseshoes, and a recreation hall with TV room and indoor games. Pets are welcome.
Phone/Fax: 504/882-5662

Description of Grounds
The park offers rental units, numerous tent spaces, RV sites with water, electric and sewer hookups, a disposal station, showers, a laundromat, and a playground for the children.

Neighboring Sights and Attractions
The Louisiana Superdome and the historic French Quarter are nearby. The world's longest causeway, crossing Lake Pontchartrain, is just 10 miles west of the club. Shops, restaurants and churches are within three miles. Motels are 5 miles, and entertainment may be found 10 miles from the park.

Honored Discounts
Twenty percent discount for AANR and NNC members.

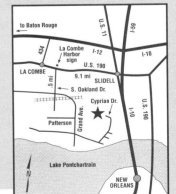

Directions
After reaching the Lacombe Harbor sign on U.S. 190, go south, follow white arrows with "La Pines" written on them. The club is two and one-half miles from U.S. 190. Ring bell at gate.

MAINE

207/583-4637

MAINE COAST SOLAR BARES

P.O. Box 104
Norway, ME 04268

 ACTIVITIES & RECREATION

General Information
A band of 100 like-minded
nudists, loosely grouped,
family-based only.
All are welcome.
Fax: 207/583-4637

Regular Meetings November
through May
Summer Travel to
Nude Parks and Beaches

Special Events
Food Feast Every November
Nude Sail on Casco Bay

POTOMAC RAMBLING BARES

MARYLAND

P.O. Box 515
Oakton, VA 22124

703/742-7987

ACTIVITIES & RECREATION

General Information
A member-run nonlanded club, Potomac
Rambling Bares explores the variety of
nude recreation opportunities available
in the greater Washington/Baltimore
area. Active year-round, the Bares
conducts at least two activities a month.
Events at members' homes include
indoor house parties, backyard
barbecues, and pool parties. Other
activities involve traveling to landed
clubs as well as private property or
public lands where nude recreation can
be enjoyed.

House Parties
Canuding on the
Potomac River
Bare Boating on
Chesapeake Bay
Murder Mysteries
Nude Beach Outings
Swim and Hot Tub
Parties

Special Events
Annual Corn Roast and Barbecue
Nude Year's Eve Celebration
Massage Workshops

FACILITIES

ACCOMMODATIONS

Wheelchair Access
Vacation Villas
■ Cabins (9)
■ Rooms (2)
Cable TV
In-room Telephone
Trailers
　heated
　w/bath
　cooking
Restaurant
Lounge
Snack Bar
Store

CAMPING

■ Tent Spaces (8)
■ R/V Spaces (4)
　● w/elec (4)
　● w/water (4)
　w/sewer
Disposal Station
■ Showers
　● cold (4)
　● hot (4)
Laundromat
■ Community Kitchen
■ Picnic Tables (6)
■ Playground
■ Pets/Leash only

RECREATION

■ Swimming Pool (30' x 60')
Lake
Whirlpool/Spa
Sauna
Exercise Equipment
Tennis
■ Volleyball
■ Shuffleboard
■ Horseshoes
Petanque
Miniten
■ Badminton
Fishing
■ Recreation Hall
■ Table Tennis
Teen Activities

■ ● denotes availability

INFORMATION

Club Personality
Maryland Health Society (MAHESO) is a family oriented nudist club conveniently located between Washington, D.C. and Baltimore, MD. Its friendly members and relaxed atmosphere make it a fine place to unwind.

Description of Grounds
MAHESO is nestled in 100 acres of pristine woodlands which back up to the Patuxent River. Its facilities include a large clubhouse with full kitchen, picnic tables between the clubhouse and the pool, grassy areas for sunbathing and leafy trees for shade.

Neighboring Sights and Attractions
Washington D.C. and the Baltimore Inner Harbor are only 35 minutes away; Annapolis, just 15 minutes from the grounds.

Honored Discounts
Twenty percent discount on grounds fees for AANR members.

Directions
Take MD 424 to Rossback Road, just prior to Route 50. Turn right on Rossback Road. In approximately 1.5 miles Rossback Road will turn sharply to the left. The road then becomes Patuxent River Road. Proceed under the overpass of U.S. Route 50 and continue for about 1 mile. MAHESO's entrance is located on the right side of the road across from a cow pasture. Look for a big mail box with club's name on it. Address is 3000 Patuxent River Road. Follow the driveway into the woods and honk when you reach the gate.

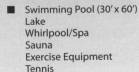

PINE TREE ASSOCIATES

1801 Hawkins Road
Crownsville, MD 21032

MARYLAND

410/841-6033

FACILITIES

ACCOMMODATIONS

- ■ Wheelchair Access
  Vacation Villas
- ■ Cabins
- ■ Rooms
  Cable TV
  In-room Telephone
  Trailers
    heated
    w/bath
    cooking
  Restaurant
  Lounge
- ■ Snack Bar
  Store

CAMPING

- ■ Tent Spaces
- ■ R/V Spaces
  - ● w/elec
  - ● w/water
    w/sewer
- ■ Disposal Station
- ■ Showers
  - ● cold
  - ● hot
- ■ Laundromat
  Community Kitchen
- ■ Picnic Tables
- ■ Playground
- ■ Pets/Leash only

RECREATION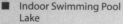

- ■ Indoor Swimming Pool
  Lake
- ■ Whirlpool/Spa
- ■ Sauna
  Exercise Equipment
- ■ Tennis
- ■ Volleyball
- ■ Shuffleboard
- ■ Horseshoes
- ■ Paddle Ball
  Miniten
  Badminton
  Fishing
- ■ Recreation Hall
- ■ Children's Activities
- ■ Teen Activities

● ■ denotes availability

INFORMATION

Club Personality
Set on 96 acres of forested hills, Pine Tree is a shady getaway just miles from the attractions of the nation's capital. Members and visitors come to Pine Tree for its beautiful setting, plentiful modern facilities, and warm family atmosphere.
Mailing Address: P.O. Box 195, Crownsville, MD 21032
Alternate Phone: 301/261-8787
Fax: 418/849-2473   E-mail: pinetr@erols.com

Description of Grounds
The club centers around a grassy common area with a pool, courts for tennis, paddleball, and volleyball, and luxuriant lawns for sunbathing. The nearby clubhouse offers a large dance floor, indoor pool and saunas, and a shady terrace for get-togethers. Overnight campers and RV owners will find ample facilities, including restrooms and showers.

Directions
Located 25 miles east of Interstate 95, and 35 miles from Washington, D.C.

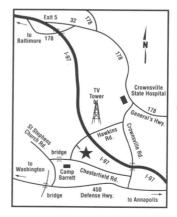

Pine

"60 years **young** and **still** going **strong**."

Neighboring Sights and Attractions

Located at the heart of one of the nation's most historic and cosmopolitan areas, Pine Tree is just 6 miles from Annapolis and less than an hour's drive from Washington, D.C. and Baltimore.

Tree Associates

PEN-MAR CLUB

P.O. Box 276
Hancock, MD 21750

MARYLAND

717/294-3262

FACILITIES

ACCOMMODATIONS

- Wheelchair Access
- Vacation Villas
- Cabins
- Rooms
- Cable TV
- In-room Telephone
- ■ Trailers (2)
  - heated
  - w/bath
  - cooking
- Restaurant
- Lounge
- Snack Bar
- Store

CAMPING

- ■ Temporary Tent Pads
- ■ R/V Spaces (10)
  - ● w/elec (10)
  - ● w/water (10)
  - w/sewer
- ■ Disposal Station
- ■ Showers (6)
  - ● cold
  - ● hot
- Laundromat
- ■ Community Kitchen
- ■ Picnic Tables (8)
- Playground
- ■ Pets/Leash only

RECREATION

- ■ Swimming Pool (20' x 40')
- ■ Pond
- ■ Fishing
- ■ Paddle Boating
- Whirlpool/Spa
- Sauna
- Exercise Equipment
- ■ Badminton
- ■ Sand Volleyball
- ■ Shuffleboard
- ■ Horseshoes
- Petanque
- Miniten
- ■ Recreation Hall
- ■ Activity Center
- Children's Activities
- ■ Hiking Trails

● denotes availability
■

INFORMATION

Club Personality
Open from May through October, the Pen-Mar Club has a membership of friendly, family oriented couples, families and singles. In operation since the 1950s, Pen-Mar is an all-volunteer cooperative, with an elected board of directors. Weekday visitors are asked to call in advance to assure themselves that a member will be available to greet them.

Description of Grounds
Pen-Mar is a natural retreat of 55 acres in the mountains along the Pennsylvania/Maryland state line. The scenic woods hold walking trails for nature lovers, and a beautiful pond for fishing, paddle-boating or just relaxing. Additionally, there are two residential areas and a camp activity center with clubhouse, heated pool, sand volleyball courts and much more.

Neighboring Sights and Attractions
Nearby are the C & O Canal, Fort Tonoloway State Park, the Coolfant Resort of Berkely Springs, and canoeing on the Potomac River.

Honored Discounts
Discounts for AANR members.

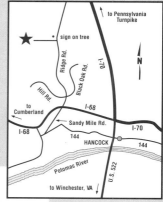

Directions
Take I-70 to Hancock, Maryland. Take a left-hand exit onto I-68 west. Take the first exit (Exit 77/Woodmont Road) and make a left at the stop sign at the end of the exit ramp. Make another left at the next stop sign onto Woodmont Road. Go about 1 mile and make a left onto Sandy Mile Road for about 3 miles. At the PA state line stay in center road and go up hill until you see yellow Pen-Mar Club sign on the left. Enter on the dirt road. Weekend visitors, after passing the gate take the left fork to the parking area.

FACILITIES

ACCOMMODATIONS

Wheelchair Access
Vacation Villas
■ Cabins (2)
Rooms
Cable TV
In-room Telephone
■ Trailers (1)
    heated
    ● w/bath
    ● cooking
Restaurant
Lounge
Snack Bar
Store

CAMPING

■ Tent Spaces (18)
■ R/V Spaces (12)
    ● w/elec
    ● w/water
    w/sewer
■ Disposal Station
■ Showers
    cold
    ● hot (1)
Laundromat
Community Kitchen
■ Picnic Tables
Playground
Pets/Leash only

RECREATION

Swimming Pool
■ Lake (1 mile)
Whirlpool/Spa
■ Sauna
Exercise Equipment
■ Tennis
■ Volleyball
■ Shuffleboard
■ Horseshoes
Petanque
■ Miniten
■ Badminton
■ Fishing
■ Clubhouse
Children's Activities
Teen Activities

INFORMATION

Club Personality
A cooperative club in continuous operation at the same location since 1950. Members of AANR and the Cape Cod Chamber of Commerce. A warm welcome is extended to couples and families seeking peace and relaxation.
Web Site: http://www.cybernude.com/stanude
E-mail: FTNANCY@aol.com or stanude@aol.com

Description of Grounds
The park has 10 rolling, wooded acres in the heart of Cape Cod, overlooking a crystal clear pond with a private sheltered beach and shaded campsites. Many of the club activities are centered around a pavilion which has picnic tables and a fire pit for cookouts.

Neighboring Sights and Attractions
Sandy Terraces is located 12 miles from Hyannis and 12 miles from Falmouth. Close to many Cape Cod beaches. Near the Cape Cod National Seashore, marinas, excellent restaurants, and entertainment spots.

Honored Discounts
Discounts for AANR, TNS, and members of many other nudist organizations.

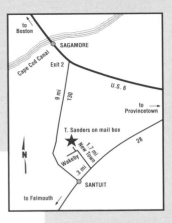

Directions
Route 6 to Exit 2, follow Route 130 south nine miles to Route 28. Turn left on Route 28 and follow for 0.3 miles. Turn left on New Town Road and follow for 1.7 miles to Wakeby Road. Turn left on Wakeby for 1,000 feet to mailbox marked "570" and "STA" signpost on the right.

312 Kittle Road
Hancock, MA 01237

413/738-5154

FACILITIES

INFORMATION

ACCOMMODATIONS

- Wheelchair Access
  Vacation Villas
- Cabins (1)
- Rooms (10)
- Cable TV
  In-room Telephone
- Trailers (4)
  - heated (4)
  - w/bath (2)
  - cooking (2)
- Restaurant
- Tavern
- Pool Bar
- 1771 Farmhouse/Four-
  Season Bed & Breakfast

CAMPING

- Tent Spaces (200)
- R/V Spaces (180)
  - w/elec (180)
  - w/water (180)
  - w/sewer (125)
- Disposal Stations (2)
- Showers
    cold
  - hot (18)
  Laundromat
  Community Kitchen
- Picnic Tables (30)
- Playground
  Pets/Leash only

RECREATION

- Solar-heated Swimming Pool
- Whirlpool/Spa
- Sauna
- Exercise Equipment
- Tennis
- Volleyball
- Shuffleboard
- Horseshoes
- Sunning Lawn
- Hiking Trails
- Petanque
- Clubhouse, DJ Dances
- Video Games
- Table Tennis
- Juke Box
- Children's Playground
- Winter Ski Packages

■ denotes availability

Club Personality

Berkshire Vista, located at the end of Kittle Road in Hancock, Berkshire County, Massachusetts, is a nude resort and campground where members and visitors can get away for a quiet, peaceful day or a lively, fun-filled weekend in the country.
Mailing Address: P.O. Box 1177, Hancock, MA 01237
Fax: 413/232-7860
Web site: http://www.tiac.net/users/aeon/bkv1.html

Description of Grounds

A high open meadow surrounded by woods on 128 private acres with pool, hot tub, sauna, sunning lawn, tennis, volleyball and more. The clubhouse offers a restaurant, bar, and DJ dances. There are campsites, trailer sites with all utilities, and lodging in motel rooms, trailer rentals, and a 1771 Country Inn.

Directions

Take Route 43 to Kittle Road, three miles from the Massachusetts/New York line, go north on Kittle Road 1.5 miles to the club's security gate; from the south (New York) take the Taconic State Parkway to Highway 295 to Route 22 to Route 43.

From the west, take the New York Thruway Exit 26 to Interstate 90 Exit 7, left on Washington Avenue, straight ahead to Route 43.

From the east (Boston), take Massachusetts Turnpike (I-90) to Route 22 (B3 Exit in New York) to Route 43. From Vermont, take Route 7 south to Route 43 south of Williamstown. Go south on Route 43, continue 7.7 miles, turn right on Kittle Road.

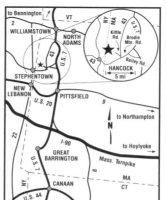

Berk

"A summer of
happy
memories
where social
nudity
is the norm."

Neighboring Sights and Attractions

Berkshire Vista is located in the finest cultural and performing arts center in the Northeast. Nearby are the Tanglewood Music Festival, summerstock playhouses, Jacobs Pillow Dance Festival, museums, ski resorts, galleries, fine dining, shopping, antiques, auction houses, racing, baseball and more.

Honored Discounts

Twenty percent discount on grounds fees for AANR and TNS members.

shire Vista Resort

MASSACHUSETTS

508/774-0339

SHERWOOD FOREST

P.O. Box 222
North Reading, MA 01864

ACTIVITIES & RECREATION

Pool, Sauna and Hot Tub Parties
Visits to Cedar Waters Village

General Information
This family oriented travel club serves all New England with winter activities such as monthly pool, sauna and hot tub parties as well as potluck lunches at various locations, mostly in Maine. During the summer most of the members are found at Cedar Waters Village, a 400-acre nudist park with a 20-acre lake, in southern New Hampshire. Write or call for more information.

SUNCHASERS

805 Chapin St.
Ludlow, MA 01056

MASSACHUSETTS

413/583-6877

ACTIVITIES & RECREATION

Weekend Camping Trips
Hot Tub and House Parties
Trips to Area Nudist Parks and
Ocean Beaches

Special Events
Nude Bowling
January Thaw Party
Spaghetti Weekend

General Information
A couples camping club which promotes social nudism for health and recreation. Year-round activities for members and invited guests. For more information call or send a stamped, self-addressed envelope.
Fax: 413/583-6877

FACILITIES

ACCOMMODATIONS

- ■ Wheelchair Access
  Vacation Villas
- ■ Cabins (1)
  Rooms
  Cable TV
  In-room Telephone
  Trailers
     heated
     w/bath
     cooking
- ■ Restaurant
  Lounge
- ■ Snack Bar
  Store

CAMPING

- ■ Tent Spaces
- ■ R/V Spaces (15)
  - ● w/elec (16)
  - ● w/water (16)
    w/sewer
- ■ Disposal Station
- ■ Showers
     cold
  - ● hot (12)
- ■ Laundromat
  Community Kitchen
- ■ Picnic Tables (25)
- ■ Playground
- ■ Pets/Leash only

RECREATION

- ■ Swimming Pool (20' x 90')
  Lake
- ■ Whirlpool/Spa
- ■ Sauna
  Exercise Equipment
  Tennis
- ■ Volleyball
- ■ Shuffleboard
- ■ Horseshoes
- ■ Petanque
  Miniten
- ■ Badminton
- ■ Recreation Hall
- ■ Billiards
- ■ Children's Activities
- ■ Teen Activities
- ■ Hiking Trails

■● denotes availability

INFORMATION

Club Personality
Open May through October, Forest Hills provides a friendly, family-focused opportunity for comfortable and discrete naturist recreation. The club is, and has been since 1953, a cooperative campground where nudists may exercise their clothing-optional choice.
Web Site: http://www.aanr.com/clubs/foresthl.html

Description of Grounds
Forest Hills is situated on 45 wooded, hilly acres in the beautiful Grand River Valley. Centrally located in lower Michigan, the club features a large heated L-shaped pool, hot tub, volleyball courts, sauna, horseshoes, shuffleboard and children's playground, as well as a clubhouse and kitchen open for breakfast and dinner on weekends.

Neighboring Sights and Attractions
Forest Hills is located half an hour west of Grand Rapids, with its hockey, baseball, museums, and other attractions. Nearby are several golf courses and fine hiking trails.

Honored Discounts
Discounts to AANR and TNS members.

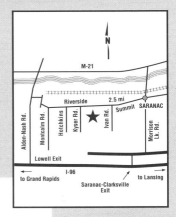

Directions
From Grand Rapids: I-96 east to Lowell exit. North to M-21. East to Jackson Street. South to Riverside Drive. East to Forest Hills Club.

MICHIGAN

313/534-8204

BARES-N-CUBS

P.O. Box 401476
Redford, MI 48240

ACTIVITIES & RECREATION

General Information
A nudist travel club with more than 300 members, Bares-N-Cubs caters primarily to couples and families. During the winter the group meets once a month at a rented health spa in Westland, Michigan.
E-mail: Gonaked@flash.net

Spa and Sauna
Swimming
Dancing
Darts and Card Games

Special Events
Nude Bowling
Trips to Landed Clubs
Nude Fishing Charters

SUNSHINE GARDENS RESORT

21901 Collier Avenue
Battle Creek, MI 49017

MICHIGAN

616/962-1600

ACCOMMODATIONS & RECREATION

Rental Cabins
RV Sites with Full Hookups
Disposal Station
Heated, Enclosed Swimming Pool
Whirlpool/Spa
Sauna
Tennis
Recreation Hall
Playground
Volleyball

Club Personality
In this clean, peaceful and friendly park, the moral code of the members stands upon a traditional, family oriented nude recreation foundation.

Description of Grounds
Sunshine Gardens Resort boasts 140 rolling, wooded acres. Camping and recreation areas hold shade trees and grassed terraces. Among other amenities are miles of nature trails, a children's playground, an indoor heated pool, swimming and fishing ponds, a spacious lodge, bathrooms with showers, and a centrally located recreation area — all screened in by nature to ensure privacy.

FACILITIES

ACCOMMODATIONS

- ■ Wheelchair Access
  Vacation Villas
  Cabins
  Rooms
- ■ Cable TV
  In-room Telephone
- ■ Trailers (4)
  - ● heated
  - ● w/bath
  - ● cooking
  Restaurant
- ■ Lounge
  Snack Bar
  Store

CAMPING

- ■ Tent Spaces (15)
- ■ R/V Spaces (100)
  - ● w/elec (85)
  - ● w/water (85)
  - ● w/sewer (85)
- ■ Disposal Station
- ■ Showers
  - ● cold (13)
  - ● hot (13)
- ■ Laundromat
  Community Kitchen
- ■ Picnic Tables (15)
- ■ Playground
- ■ Pets/Leash only

RECREATION

- ■ Heated Swimming Pool
  Lake
- ■ Whirlpool/Spa
- ■ Sauna
- ■ Exercise Equipment
- ■ Tennis (2)
- ■ Volleyball
- ■ Shuffleboard
- ■ Horseshoes (2)
- ■ Petanque (2)
- ■ Softball Diamond
- ■ Badminton
- ■ Fishing
- ■ Recreation Hall
- ■ Children's/Teen Activities
- ■ Croquet
- ■ Basketball

■ ● denotes availability

INFORMATION

Club Personality
Upscale, professional, major city suburban resort with all the amenities.
Alternate Phone: 248/628-7200
Fax: 248/628-0512

Description of Grounds
Whispering Oaks is situated on 52 rolling, wooded acres with open sunning areas, that are well-manicured and well-landscaped. The club also has a 1.5 acre pond stocked with trout and bass.

Neighboring Sights and Attractions
Michigan is host to Mo-town, world famous Green Field Village Ford Museum, Greek Town, and great dinning. Canada is 40 miles away.

Honored Discounts
Discounts for all AANR members.

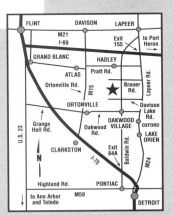

Directions
When driving north of Detroit on Interstate 75, take Exit 84 (A), Baldwin Road, north 13.5 miles to the gate. When driving from the north on Interstate 75, take Interstate 69 east from Flint to Lapeer Road (M-24), Exit 155, go south, follow map to club gate.

MICHIGAN

8700 W. 6¹/₂ Road
Mesick, MI 49668

TRAVERSE AREA NATURISTS

General Information

Traverse Area Naturists (TAN) members are from throughout the entire state of Michigan. A nonlanded club at present, gatherings are held in members' homes utilizing hot tubs and saunas. A family oriented club, welcoming inquiries from families, couples and singles. Plans are being made to have a landed club by 1999 with pool, hot tub, volleyball and cabins. Write for more information.

ACTIVITIES & RECREATION

Hot Tub and Sauna Parties
Potlucks and Board Games
Cross Country Skiing

Visits to Landed Clubs and Otter Creek Beach, part of the Sleeping Bear Dunes National Lakeshore

TURTLE LAKE RESORT

2101 Nine Mile Road
Union City, MI 49094

MICHIGAN

517/741-7004

ACTIVITIES & RECREATION

Clubhouse with Indoor Pool and Hot Tub
Dances/Family Events
Lake Frontage
202 RV Sites/Room Rentals
Food Service and Camp Store
Special Group Rates

Special Events
Annual Antique Car Show
Annual Motorcycle Rally

General Information

Michigan's year-round family clothing-optional resort, Turtle Lake Resort offers an all weather recreation facility. With 160-acres of modern camping and a year-round 10,000 square-foot clubhouse. Outdoor activities include fishing, boating, volleyball, shuffleboard. The club offers many winter indoor and outdoor activities. Also enjoy the spiritual area at the Tipi for relaxation and meditation. Located in central lower Michigan they are an easy travel from Chicago, Detroit and Toledo. Call for weekend special events which includes dances and family activities.

Mailing address: P.O. Box 55, Union City, MI 49094
Fax: 517/741-7919

P.O. Box 580950
Minneapolis, MN 55458

612/434-4922

FACILITIES

INFORMATION

ACCOMMODATIONS

- ■ Wheelchair Access
  Vacation Villas
  Cabins)
  Rooms
  Cable TV
  In-room Telephone
- ■ Trailers (3)
  - ● heated (3)
  - ● w/bath (2)
  - ● cooking (3)
  Restaurant
  Lounge
  Snack Bar
  Store
- ■ Ice

CAMPING

- ■ Tent Spaces (5)
- ■ R/V Spaces (5)
  - ● w/elec
  - ● w/water
  - ● w/sewer
  Disposal Station
- ■ Showers
  cold
  - ● hot (7)
- ■ Laundromat
- ■ Community Kitchen
- ■ Picnic Tables (10)
- ■ Playground
- ■ Pets/Leash only

RECREATION

- ■ Swimming Pool (26' x 60')
  Lake
- ■ Whirlpool/Spa
- ■ Sauna
  Exercise Equipment
  Tennis
- ■ Volleyball
  Shuffleboard
- ■ Horseshoes
  Petanque
  Miniten
  Badminton
  Fishing
- ■ Recreation Hall
- ■ Children's Activities
- ■ Teen Activities

■● denotes availability

Club Personality
Open May 15 through September 15, Avatan is a friendly, family oriented resort just 30 miles from Minneapolis. Pets on a leash are welcome.
Web Site: http://www.aanr.com/aanr-mn.htm

Description of Grounds
Avatan is a clean and well-tended resort, rolling and wooded, with a picnic area and large, grassy sunning areas, newly renovated volleyball courts, and one of the finest swimming areas in the upper Midwest.

Neighboring Sights and Attractions
Nearby are a selection of excellent restaurants, movies, churches and other activities. The sports and entertainment centers of Minneapolis/St. Paul are only 30 minutes away. There is easy access to the Mall of America, the world's largest shopping facility.

Honored Discounts
Discounts to all AANR members.

Directions
From Interstate 94 Bypass (Interstate 694) north on Minnesota Highway 65 to Sims Road (210th Street N.E.), west 1.2 miles to 524 Sims Road.

FACILITIES

ACCOMMODATIONS

- ■ Wheelchair Access
  Vacation Villas
  Cabins
  Rooms
  Cable TV
  In-room Telephone
- ■ Trailers (2)
  - heated
  - w/bath
  - cooking
  Restaurant
  Lounge
  Snack Bar
  Store

CAMPING

- ■ Tent Spaces (10)
- ■ R/V Spaces (2)
  - ● w/elec
  - ● w/water
  - w/sewer
  Disposal Station
- ■ Showers
  - ● cold (8)
  - ● hot (8)
  Laundromat
- ■ Community Kitchen
- ■ Picnic Tables (4)
- ■ Playground
- ■ Pets/Leash only

RECREATION

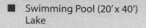

- ■ Swimming Pool (20' x 40')
  Lake
  Whirlpool/Spa
- ■ Sauna (2)
  Exercise Equipment
  Tennis
- ■ Volleyball
- ■ Shuffleboard
- ■ Horseshoes
- ■ Petanque
  Miniten
- ■ Badminton
  Fishing
- ■ Recreation Hall
- ■ Darts
- ■ Table Tennis

■ ● denotes availability

INFORMATION

Club Personality
Oakwood is a cooperative club, with members hosting or participating in various social activities during the May-through-September season. Every Saturday and Sunday most members gather on the common grounds for swimming, sunning, conversation and volleyball. Visitors soon become part of this friendly group.
Alternate phone: 612/462-8694
Web Site: oneofspm@aol.com

Description of Grounds
This 40-acre club is surrounded by the Carlos Avery Game Refuge, farmland and forests. Amenities include a large sunning area with swimming pool, volleyball courts, saunas, and restrooms with adjacent showers. There are 50 lots for lease by members.

Neighboring Sights and Attractions
Restaurants, gas stations, a grocery store and more are located 4 miles away in Wyoming, Minnesota. Movie theaters are between 8 and 11 miles away, and Minneapolis and St. Paul are approximately 30 to 35 miles away.

Honored Discounts
Twenty percent discount for AANR members.

SNO-BIRDS

MINNESOTA

P.O. Box 32034
Minneapolis, MN 55432

ACTIVITIES &
RECREATION

Winter Snowmobiling, Skiing and
Hot Tubbing
Visits to Nudist Parks
Weekend Campouts
Swim Parties
Regular Winter Get-Togethers
at a Health Club
Social Gatherings Both
Winter and Summer

General Information
Serving the Minnesota and
surrounding areas, the Sno-Birds
hold organized activities year-
round. Travel information is
furnished to members. For
information write to the club.

MISSOURI

314/966-3377

BARE HUNTERS

P.O. Box 9971
St. Louis, MO 63122

ACTIVITIES &
RECREATION

General Information
Bare Hunters travel club
meets twice a month, all
year-round. Couples,
children and singles are
welcome.

Bowling
Swimming
Health Club Activities:
"Walleyball"
Racquet Ball
Fitness Machines
Saunas

Special Events
Hibernation Celebration—Fall
Nude Year Event—Spring

FORTY ACRE CLUB

MISSOURI

P.O. Box 309
Lonedell, MO 63060

314/629-0050

FACILITIES

ACCOMMODATIONS

- ■ Wheelchair Access
- Vacation Villas
- Cabins
- ■ Rooms (4)
- Cable TV
- In-room Telephone
- Trailers
  - heated
  - w/bath
  - cooking
- Restaurant
- Lounge
- ■ Snack Bar
- Store

CAMPING

- ■ Tent Spaces (9)
- ■ R/V Spaces (10)
  - ● w/elec
  - ● w/water
  - w/sewer
- Disposal Station
- ■ Showers
  - ● cold (1)
  - ● hot
- ■ Laundromat
- ■ Community Kitchen
- ■ Picnic Tables (40)
- ■ Playground
- ■ Pets/Leash only

RECREATION

- ■ Swimming Pool (20' x 40')
- ■ Lake
- Whirlpool/Spa
- Sauna
- Exercise Equipment
- ■ Tennis
- ■ Volleyball
- ■ Shuffleboard
- ■ Horseshoes
- Petanque
- Miniten
- Badminton
- ■ Fishing
- ■ Recreation Hall
- ■ Children's Activities
- ■ Teen Activities
- ■ Darts

■ ● denotes availability

INFORMATION

Club Personality
The Forty Acre Club, nicknamed "America's Gateway Family Nudist Club" for its proximity to the famous Gateway Arch in St. Louis, is a friendly, year-round, family oriented resort where nice things happen—including an annual fall pig roast and new members' party.

Description of Grounds
The club boasts an attractive clubhouse with color satellite TV, pool table, darts, a beautiful rock fireplace, and a large kitchen for dinner parties. On the grounds there are hiking trails, large tent sites, 10 RV sites with electricity and water, community kitchen, showers, laundromat, playground for the kids, swimming pool and fishing lake.

Neighboring Sights and Attractions
Meramac Caverns, Six Flags over Mid-America, St. Louis Zoo, Cardinal's baseball, Missouri wine country and the Riverport Amphitheater.

Honored Discounts
Discounts for AANR, NNC and FCN members.

Directions
Located off Interstate 44, 30 miles west of St. Louis at Lonedell, Missouri. See map for directions. Mailbox Number 41 on Weida Road, Road Number WA3-270. Call or write to the club for more information.

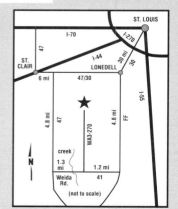

OZARK LEISURE CLUB

MISSOURI

3237 E. Sunshine, Ste. A, #183
Springfield, MO 65804

417/886-4137

ACTIVITIES & RECREATION

Visiting Landed Clubs
Year-round House Parties
Pontoon Boat Parties
Lake Gatherings

General Information
Ozark Leisure Club is a nonlanded family club that does not discriminate against singles. At present, the club is majority of couples from throughout the Ozark region. The club meets once a month at a member's home. They invite guests and new-comers. Their motto is "Wear a smile and bring a towel."

Special Events
November Club Anniversary
Halloween Party

NEBRASKA

CORNHUSKER RECREATION CLUB

P.O. Box 31326
Omaha, NE 68131-0326

ACTIVITIES & RECREATION

General Information
The Cornhusker Recreation Club is a nonlanded AANR club serving Nebraska and Western Iowa. As a family oriented club, it welcomes couples and children of all ages.

Trips to Landed Clubs
Skinnydipping
Pool Parties
Hot Tubbing
Potlucks

Special Events
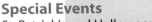
St. Patrick's and Halloween Parties

LAS VEGAS SUN CLUB

NEVADA

P.O. Box 12322
East Las Vegas, NV 89112

702/723-5463

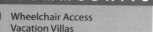

FACILITIES

ACCOMMODATIONS

- Wheelchair Access
  Vacation Villas
- Cabins (2)
  Rooms
  Cable TV
  In-room Telephone
- Trailers (2)
  - heated
    w/bath
    cooking
  Restaurant
  Lounge
  Snack Bar
- Store (Limited Sundries)
- Microwaveable Sandwiches

CAMPING

- Tent Spaces (3)
- R/V Spaces (5)
  - w/elec
  - w/water
    w/sewer
- Disposal Station
- Showers
    cold
  - hot (6)
- Laundromat
- Community Kitchen
  Picnic Tables
  Playground
- Pets/Leash only

RECREATION

- Swimming Pool (15' x 32')
  Lake
- Whirlpool/Spa
- Sauna
  Exercise Equipment
  Tennis
  Volleyball
- Shuffleboard
- Horseshoes
- Petanque
  Miniten
  Badminton
  Fishing
  Recreation Hall
  Children's Activities
  Teen Activities

■ ● denotes availability

INFORMATION

Club Personality

Las Vegas Sun Club is located in the desert community of Sandy Valley, Nevada. The club has small creatures living on the grounds, so shoes or thongs should be worn at all times. Las Vegas Sun Club is family oriented, but not clothing-optional.

Toll Free: 888/SUNLVSC   Fax: 702/723-1451
E-mail: lvsc@juno.com

Description of Grounds

The club sits on three acres of desert land, with RV sites, nonsmoking cabins, trailers, a clubhouse, numerous trees, and a 10,000 square-foot lawn and sunning area. There is a walkway to the top of Observatory Hill, with a view of Sandy Valley, majestic mountains, and night stargazing.

Neighboring Sights and Attractions

Las Vegas, with its gambling resorts, is only 50 miles away, while Prim, Nevada's newest town, with gambling, restaurants and golf courses is just 35 miles away. Jean, Nevada, with hotels, gaming and a private airport, is only 25 miles from the resoRT

Honored Discounts

Discounts to naturists and card carrying members of AANR.

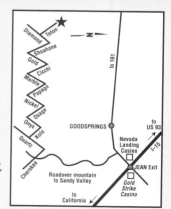

Directions

Exit from I-15 south to California at Jean, NV, go west toward Good Springs. Turn left at Sandy Valley sign. Go over Mountain range, turn right at first road (Cherokee). Make a left on Quartz. Turn right onto Kolo, follow paved road with many left and right turns (approximately 6 miles). Turn right onto Teton, go to the top of the road to the double wide trailer (RVs on left side of the lane). For a detailed map, write or call the club.

ROADRUNNER NATURISTS

P.O. Box 956
Los Alamos, NM 87544

NEW MEXICO

505/662-3618

ACTIVITIES & RECREATION

Swimming Parties
Hot Tubbing
Picnics and Potlucks
Camping in National Forests
Hot Springs Trips
Visits to Nudist Resorts

General Information
This family oriented travel club is based in the sun-drenched mountains of northern New Mexico. An interesting variety of monthly activities take club members far and wide, even to neighboring states, and AANR and The Naturist Society visitors are welcome on these outings. Please write or call for information.

NEW MEXICO

505/522-6284

SUNTREE TRAVEL CLUB

Suite 182–2000 E. Lohman #110
Las Cruces, NM 88001

ACTIVITIES & RECREATION

General Information
SunTree Travel Club is an eclectic band of nudists, formed—as the result of several spinoffs—from the old club nicknamed "The Mulberry Tree Gang." This diverse group of unlikely friends enjoys visiting area landed clubs and nude sites, as well as talking and eating. Younger members are influencing the sedentary segment into a more active lifestyle, but don't expect a SunTree Olympic Team.
Fax: 505/522-6284
E-mail: rrichey@delphi.com

Visits to Neighboring Clubs
Swimming and Hot Tubbing
Potlucks
Hot Springs
Camping
Discussion Groups

Special Events
Winterfest in November
Annual October Birthday and Halloween Haunting
Spring and/or Fall Visit to a Landed Club

NEW JERSEY

P.O. Box 438
Navesink, NJ 07752

FRIENDS OF GUNNISON

General Information
The mission of Friends of Gunnison (FoG) is to foster community and fun among the members. Membership is drawn exclusively from Gunnison Beach on Sandy Hook, New Jersey. In addition to social events and a monthly newsletter, this nonlanded club maintains an ongoing dialogue with the National Park Service and other members of the Sandy Hook community, in order to protect and improve naturist recreation.
E-mail: foghornnj@aol.com

ACTIVITIES & RECREATION

Nude Cruises in Sandy Hook Bay
Off-Season Pool Parties at Area Health Club
Trips to Landed Clubs
Concerts and Parties on Gunnison Beach, Sandy Hook, New Jersey
Monthly Newsletter, *The FoGHorn*

THE ROAD WARRIORS

ACTIVITIES & RECREATION

Volleyball Tournaments
Nude Beach Visits
Camping and Cookouts
Visits to Landed Clubs

Special Events
Attending ESA and AANR Conventions

NEW JERSEY

P.O. Box 105
Mays Landing, NJ 08330

General Information
The Road Warriors, a volleyball-oriented travel club, was formed for players, friends, fans and lovers of volleyball. The club participates in the Tri-State League, playing matches at Pine Tree near Annapolis, Maryland; White Thorn near Darlington, Pennsylvania; Sunny Rest near Palmerton, Pennsylvania; Penn Sylvan near Reading, Pennsylvania and Avalon near Paw Paw, West Virginia. Club players attend the Superbowl and have won trophies in most divisions. Families, couples and singles are welcome to join and travel with the club.

ROCK LODGE CLUB

NEW JERSEY

P.O. Box 86
Stockholm, NJ 07460

973/697-9721

FACILITIES

ACCOMMODATIONS

- Wheelchair Access
- Vacation Villas
- ■ Cabins
- ■ Rooms
- Cable TV
- In-room Telephone
- Trailers
  - heated
  - w/bath
  - cooking
- Restaurant
- Lounge
- Snack Bar
- Store

CAMPING

- Tent Spaces
- R/V Spaces
  - w/elec
  - w/water
  - w/sewer
- Disposal Station
- ■ Showers (4)
  - cold
  - ● hot
- ■ Laundromat
- ■ Community Kitchen
- ■ Picnic Tables (15)
- ■ Playground
- Pets/Leash only

RECREATION

- Swimming Pool
- ■ Lake (5 acres)
- ■ Whirlpool/Spa
- ■ Sauna
- Exercise Equipment
- ■ Tennis
- ■ Volleyball
- Shuffleboard
- Horseshoes
- Petanque
- ■ Badminton
- ■ Fishing
- ■ Recreation Hall
- ■ Children's Activities
- ■ Teen Activities
- ■ Sunday Get-togethers
- ■ Holiday Parties/Dances

■ ● denotes availability

INFORMATION

Club Personality
Rock Lodge Club has over one hundred acres of pristine woodlands, a five acre spring-fed lake, and the second highest elevation in the state of New Jersey. Write or call for a visit to this family and couples oriented, membership-based club.

Description of Grounds
Rock Lodge Club has a five-acre lake for swimming, sunning, boating and fishing, as well as courts for tennis badminton, and volleyball. Additionally, there are a children's playground, a recreation hall with table tennis, two community living rooms with fireplaces, a library, and several historic buildings. Guest rooms and cabins are available.

Neighboring Sights and Attractions
There are motel accommodations, fine restaurants and shopping areas close by, and a large county park with camping sites and hiking trails within five miles. New Jersey's largest water theme park is just minutes away.

Honored Discounts
Discounts for AANR and The Naturist Society members.

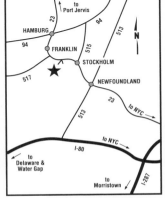

Directions
From New York City: From Lincoln Tunnel take RT 3 west for 12 miles to RT 46 west for 3.5 miles to RT 46, 80 and 23 interchange. Go north on RT 23 for 21 miles to Stockholm (Jorgensen's Restaurant). Just past Jorgensen's, turn left at blinker (Lake Stockholm sign). Go one-half mile and take right fork. Go one mile to Rock Lodge gate on the left. Ring bell.

NEW JERSEY

P.O. Box 1470
West Caldwell, NJ 07007

SOLARAMBLERS

General Information
This family oriented club serves the Metropolitan New York area. The club meets year-round, but is most active in the winter months when camps and beaches are closed and nudists seek alternative activities. Inquiries are welcome.

ACTIVITIES & RECREATION

Family Spa Parties
House Parties
Hotel and Travel Discounts

SUN AIRS OF NEW JERSEY

P.O. Box 228
New Milford, NJ 07646

NEW JERSEY

908/850-1300

ACTIVITIES & RECREATION

Swimming
Volleyball
Badminton
Picnicking
Camping
Ping Pong
Shuffleboard
Hot Tub

General Information
Although Sun Airs is a travel club, it uses the grounds of Goodland Country Club in Hackettstown, New Jersey as its landed club. Goodland, which has been in existence for over 65 years, is centrally located in the Tri-State area and is easily accessible from most points. Sunairs welcomes new members who wish to join the AANR.

NEW JERSEY
908/689-4911

TRI STATE SUN CLUB
P.O. Box 532NG
Broadway, NJ 08808

ACTIVITIES & RECREATION

General Information
With members in 46 states, Tri State Sun club is one of AANR's largest clubs. Although family oriented, Tri State Sun Club does welcome singles and couples, and many of its events are clothing-optional. The projected date for the opening of its new club in southeast New York State's Hudson Valley Region is May 1, 1997. The club's newsletter will carry details.
Home number: 908/689-1048

Nude Olym-Pick Games
Volleyball
Indoor Swim Socials in Winter Months
Pig Roasts

TRI-STATE METRO NATURISTS
P.O. Box 1317
New York, NY 10150

NEW JERSEY
215/379-1239

ACTIVITIES & RECREATION

Tall Ship Cruises
Annual Nude Dinner Cruise
Indoor/Dinner/Dance/Swim Parties
Beach Festivals
Group Trips to Area Resorts
Canuding
Hiking
Family Acitivities
Singles Nights

Founded in 1981, TSMN is a politically active organization with social activities for its members. With members in over 17 states, TSMN's purpose is to educate, promote and establish clothing-optional recreation sites. Over the years the club has faced many challenges to protect nude beaches such as Sandy Hook where members have developed a good working relationship with the National Park Service.

TSMN is comprised of people from every walk of life, people who enjoy the camaraderie and fun of belonging. Families, couples, and singles welcome.

FACILITIES

ACCOMMODATIONS

- ■ Wheelchair Access
  - Vacation Villas
  - Cabins
  - Rooms
  - Cable TV
  - In-room Telephone
- ■ Trailers (3)
  - ● heated
    - w/bath
  - ● cooking
  - Restaurant
- ■ Lounge
- ■ Snack Bar
- ■ Store

CAMPING

- ■ Tent Spaces (10)
- ■ R/V Spaces (40)
  - ● w/elec
  - ● w/water
  - w/sewer
- ■ Disposal Station
- ■ Showers (7)
  - cold
  - ● hot
  - Laundromat
  - Community Kitchen
- ■ Picnic Tables
- ■ Playground
- ■ Pets/Leash only

RECREATION

- Swimming Pool
- ■ Lake (4.5 acres)
- ■ Whirlpool/Spa
  - Sauna
- ■ Exercise Equipment
  - Tennis
- ■ Volleyball
  - Shuffleboard
- ■ Horseshoes
  - Petanque
  - Miniten
- ■ Badminton
- ■ Fishing
- ■ Recreation Hall
  - Children's Activities
  - Teen Activities

■ ● denotes availability

INFORMATION

Club Personality
The Buckridge atmosphere of peace and tranquility is conducive to the making of new and lasting friends.
Web Site: http://www.spectra.net/~nudist
E-mail: nudist@cheerful.com

Description of Grounds
Buckridge is a wooded campground with a four and a half acre lake. Facilities are well maintained and spotlessly clean. Gardens and grass areas provide a pleasant sunning experience.

Neighboring Sights and Attractions
Within reasonable driving distance are the Tioga Scenic Railroad Excursion, Corning Glass, science centers, go-kart track, an eighteen hole golf course, Harris Hill Soaring, Watkins Glen Auto Racing, Finger Lakes Dinner Cruises, rodeo, and gardens.

Honored Discounts
25 percent discount on daily rates for AANR members. 40 percent discount on four-hour passes.

Directions
From Owego exit at #64 off 17, take 96 to Candor. Approximately one mile west of Candor, take Tuttle Hill Road for 3/4 mile. Camp is on the left. From Ithaca take 96B to Candor, then 96 toward Spencer to Tuttle Hill Road.

FACILITIES

ACCOMMODATIONS

- Wheelchair Access (Limited)
  Vacation Villas
- Cabins (5)
  Rooms
  Cable TV
  In-room Telephone
- Trailers (2)
  - heated
  - w/bath
  - cooking
- Restaurant
  Lounge
- Snack Bar
  Store

CAMPING

- Tent Spaces (50)
- R/V Spaces (75)
  - w/elec
  - w/water
  w/sewer
- Disposal Station
- Showers
  cold
  - hot (6)
  Laundromat
  Community Kitchen
- Picnic Tables (30)
- Playground
- Pets/Leash only

RECREATION

- Swimming Pool (25' x 50')
  Lake
- Whirlpool/Spa (2)
- Sauna
  Exercise Equipment
  Tennis
- Volleyball
- Shuffleboard
- Horseshoes
- Petanque
- Hiking Trails
- Badminton
- Fishing
- Recreation Hall
- Children's Activities
- Teen Activities
- Planned Weekend Activities

INFORMATION

Club Personality

Empire Haven is nestled on 97 beautiful acres in the Finger Lakes Region of New York State. A great place for families, couples and singles to spend a relaxing day or weekend in a stress free environment. Open May 1 through September 30.
Fax: 315/497-1989
E-mail: mrobin2459@aol.com

Description of Grounds

Heated pool, sauna, two whirlpools, playground, fishing, volleyball, petanque, shuffleboard, horseshoes, library, a pavilion for dances and other social activities, hiking trails, large, well-maintained campsites, clean park areas and a spacious lawn for sunning.

Neighboring Sights and Attractions

Shops and churches are 5 miles, restaurants 3 miles, and motels and entertainment 10 miles from the park in the city of Cortland, New York. Many nearby places for sight seeing.

Honored Discounts

Discounts for AANR, INF, TNS, Canadian affiliates, and other card carrying nudist group members.

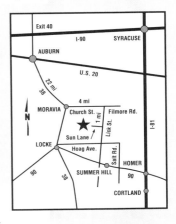

Directions

From Moravia turn east on Church Street (post office on the corner), go four miles to Lick Street, turn south (right), go one mile to Sun Lane, turn right, the second drive on the right. From Homer take 90N past Summer Hill to Country Kitchen, turn right on Lick Street, go two and one-half miles, then take a left on Sun Lane, the second drive on the right. Late arrivals, please call ahead for gate access.

NEW YORK

716/825-4064

FRIENDS OF BUFFALO

P.O. Box 2468
Buffalo, NY 14240-2468

General Information
A travel club that visits landed clubs on holidays and other occasions. At least once a month there is a special event—such as a '50s Sockhop, Wine and Cheese Party or a Caribbean Party, where members, prospective members and guests enjoy each other's company. Families and couples are welcome, single gentlemen on a limited basis.

ACTIVITIES & RECREATION

Bowling
Darts and Billiards
Wine and Cheese Party
Visiting Landed Clubs
Camping and Hiking Nude

Special Events
Potluck Meetings
House Parties

FULL-TAN SUN CLUB

1350 Carlisle Road
Sprakers, NY 12166

NEW YORK

518/673-2886

ACCOMMODATIONS & RECREATION

RV Sites with Electric
Swimming Pool
Volleyball
Horseshoes
Badminton
Recreation Hall
Children/Family Activities
Community Kitchen

Club Personality
The Full-Tan Sun Club is located in the heart of the beautiful Mohawk Valley. The club is primarily a family-oriented park, with membership available for families and couples only. All applicants are carefully screened, to provide safety and privacy for members. Visitors should write for information before visiting the camp.

Description of Grounds
Full-Tan Sun Club is situated on 80 secluded acres. There is a clubhouse for games, movies, music, social activities, sauna and TV. Also available are hiking, fishing, and sunning on a 20-acre lawn. The club has a playground for the kids, horseshoes, volleyball and badminton.

NEW YORK

518/945-1399

HUDSON VALLEY NATURALLY

P.O. Box 1
Athens, NY 12015

ACTIVITIES & RECREATION

General Information
A family oriented clothing-optional camping retreat with nudity required in the pool only. There are two lakes and 60 acres of wooded and sunning areas.

Neighboring Sights and Attractions
Catskill Game Farm
Historical Sites, Museums, Antique Shops, Festivals, Fairs, Tours, Dining Out, River Cruises

Special Events
Annual Nude Olym-Pick Games
Artist Weekends

RV and Tent Sites
Two Lakes: one for quiet zone, one for activities and swimming
Heated Converstion Pool
Large Pavilion
Fire Ring
Canoes and Rowboats
Softball Field
Volleyball
Horseshoes

LONG ISLAND TRAVASUNS

NEW YORK

P.O. Box 250
Wantagh, NY 11793

516/679-6942

ACTIVITIES & RECREATION

Pool Parties
House Parties
Trips to Landed Clubs
Christmas Walk in New York City

General Information
Family travel club with members from Long Island and New York Tri-State Area. Activities are open to visitors members of other clubs and visitors.

Special Events
Annual Membership and Elections
Beach Gatherings
Pool Parties in Winter Months

NEW YORK

716/244-1219

ROCHESTER NATURIST SOCIETY

237 Vassar Street
Rochester, NY 14607

General Information
Rochester Naturist Society, where families, couples, singles and children are always welcome, is a year-round socially and politically active group. In warm weather, members visit Steph's Pond, Empire Haven and area beaches. In cool weather, members hold swim evenings at a YMCA, and parties at members' homes. An indoor pool, sauna and spa are regularly available. Write or call for information.
Fax: 716/442-1838

ACTIVITIES & RECREATION

Activities and Recreation
Indoor and Outdoor Swimming
Whirlpool Spa, and Sauna
Volleyball and Children's Activities
Camping
Massage
Parties

Special Events
Sponsor Naturist Gatherings
Mystery and Holiday Parties

THE SKINNYDIPPERS

51-04 39th Avenue
Woodside, NY 11377

NEW YORK

718/651-4689

ACTIVITIES & RECREATION

Nude Beach Parties
Visits to Nudist Resorts
Nude and Clothed Nature Walks
Weekend Massage
Workshops
Nude Spa Parties
House and Dance Parties

Annual Events
Nude Cruise in New York Harbor
Nude Cocktail Party in Manhattan Art Gallery
Nude Kite Flying, Body Painting

General Information
This large nudist travel club schedules numerous social events for singles and couples, averaging six per weekend in winter and twelve per weekend in summer. The quarterly calendar also lists selected activities for 24 other nudist clubs in nearby states. Call or write for a free copy of the schedule and/or newsletter.
Fax: 718/424-1883

NEW YORK

716/352-8713

General Information
Small, but growing club which offers a secure environment and a nearly equal gender ratio. Singles and couples welcome for coffee prior to joining the club.
E-mail: EECKHOUT@Frontiernet.net

SUNFUN

P.O. Box 26418
Rochester, NY 14626

ACTIVITIES & RECREATION

Hot Tub/Pool Parties
Travel to Various Nude Locations

SUN RANGERS

P.O. Box 2031
Blasdell, NY 14219

ACTIVITIES & RECREATION

Camping and Hiking
Picnics and Potlucks
Trips to Landed Clubs
Group Excursions
Casino Trips

NEW YORK

716/743-8514

General Information
Founded in 1992, the Sun Rangers is a small nonlanded club serving western New York State. The club offers interested individuals the opportunity to participate in nudist activities without the expense of unwanted extras.

313 Bar-S-Trail
Reidsville, NC 27320

910/349-2456

FACILITIES

INFORMATION

ACCOMMODATIONS

Wheelchair Access
Vacation Villas
■ Cabins (1)
■ Rooms (2)
Cable TV
In-room Telephone
■ Trailers (1)
  ● heated
    w/bath
    cooking
Restaurant
Lounge
■ Snack Bar
Store

CAMPING

■ Tent Spaces
■ R/V Spaces
  ● w/elec (2)
  ● w/water (2)
  w/sewer
Disposal Station
■ Showers
  ● cold (4)
  ● hot (4)
Laundromat
■ Community Kitchen
■ Picnic Tables (30)
Playground
Pets/Leash only

RECREATION

■ Swimming Pool (18' x 36')
■ Lake (6 acres)
■ Whirlpool/Spa
■ Sauna
Exercise Equipment
Tennis
■ Volleyball
Shuffleboard
■ Horseshoes
Petanque
Miniten
Badminton
■ Fishing
■ Recreation Hall
Children's Activities
Teen Activities
■ Nature Trails

● denotes availability
■

Club Personality

The Bar-S-Ranch caters primarily to families and couples, although singles are admitted as permitted by a gender ratio. The membership has a reputation for being friendly and welcoming new visitors.
Web Site: http://www.cybernude.com/bar/s/ranch

Description of Grounds

The Bar-S-Ranch is located in the gently rolling hills of the Piedmont of North Carolina, just north of Greensboro. The grounds consist of 178 acres, a beautiful spring-fed lake, and well-manicured lawns offering both sunny and shaded areas. The property provides natural privacy while offering spacious activity areas amid all manner of flora and fauna.

Neighboring Sights and Attractions

Old Salem in Winston, Salem, and Chinqua-Penn Plantation in Reidsville offer interesting diversions, while North Carolina's numerous golf courses—two within 4 miles—challenge the pros. The spring and fall International Furniture Shows are in High Point.

Honored Discounts

Discounts for AANR, TNS and ANSP members.

Directions

From I-85/I-40 in Greensboro get on U.S. 29 north and go to Cone Blvd.-west. On Cone Blvd. travel west to the fourth red light which will be Church Street. Turn right on Church Street and go north approximately 13 miles to the second stop sign which will be U.S. 158. At U.S.158 turn left and go 0.6 miles to Bar-S-Trail on the right. Note: The Bar-S-Trail intersects U.S. 158 at two places. The entrance to the park is on the east leg of the loop. Turn right down the Bar-S-Trail to the entrance gate 1/2 mile back.

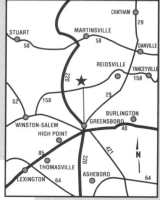

NIRVANA SUN RESORT

NORTH CAROLINA

65 Harbour Drive
Tabor City, NC 28463

800/378-7072

ACCOMMODATIONS & RECREATION

Four-room Bed & Breakfast
Swimming and Volleyball Pools
Oversized Whirlpool/Spa
Tennis Courts Coming Spring '98
Dances Every Other Weekend
Special Occasion Parties
Clubhouse

General Information
Located two miles from Tabor City, North Carolina, Nirvana Sun Resort is situated on 39 acres—home to 36 permanent trailer sites. Eight pull-through sites with full hookups are available for visitors and short stopovers. The resort is near 108 golf courses, and just 27 miles from Myrtle Beach. Convenient for fly-ins, Twin City Airport is three miles from the grounds. Complimentary airport pickup is provided.
Local phone: 910/653-9065
Fax: 910/653-9503

NORTH CAROLINA

704/565-5023

NORTH CAROLINA NATURISTS

P.O. Box 33845
Charlotte, NC 28233

ACTIVITIES & RECREATION

General Information
The North Carolina Naturists is one of the most active nonlanded clubs in the country. Boasting members across the region, most events occur within a three hour drive from Charlotte. For additional information about club activities, special interest groups or publications write or call the club.

Camping Trips—private property and national forests
Trips to Landed Clubs
Pool Parties
Halloween Bash
Hot Tub and
Theme Parties

Special Events
Biannual Grill-offs With Awards
Annual Casino Party

WHISPERING PINES | NORTH CAROLINA

1114 Sun Street
Ocean Isle Beach, NC 28469

910/287-6404

FACILITIES

ACCOMMODATIONS

- ■ Wheelchair Access
  Vacation Villas
  Cabins
  Rooms
- ■ Cable TV
  In-room Telephone
- ■ Trailers (8)
  - ● heated
  - ● w/bath
  - ● cooking
  Restaurant
  Lounge
  Snack Bar
  Store

CAMPING

- ■ Tent Spaces (80)
- ■ R/V Spaces (43)
  - ● w/elec
  - ● w/water
  - ● w/sewer
- ■ Disposal Station
- ■ Showers
  - ● cold (8)
  - ● hot (8)
  Laundromat
  Community Kitchen
- ■ Picnic Tables (18)
- ■ Playground
- ■ Pets/Leash only

RECREATION

- ■ Swimming Pool (20' x 40')
- ■ Lake (1 acre)
- ■ Whirlpool/Spa
- ■ Sauna
  Exercise Equipment
  Tennis
- ■ Volleyball
- ■ Shuffleboard
- ■ Horseshoes
  Petanque
  Miniten
  Badminton
- ■ Fishing
- ■ Recreation Hall
  Children's Activities
  Teen Activities

■ ● denotes availability

INFORMATION

Club Personality
Located 17 miles north of North Myrtle Beach, South Carolina, Whispering Pines is Christian owned and operated, family oriented, conservative, quiet and relaxing.
888/LUV2TAN (888/588-2826)

Description of Grounds
Whispering Pines consists of 15 acres of sky-high pines and grassy sunning areas, with an additional 13 acres of nature trails winding through the pines.

Neighboring Sights and Attractions
The resort is twenty-five miles from Myrtle Beach, South Carolina, and seven miles from Sunset Beach, North Carolina.

Honored Discounts
Discounts to AANR, NNC and TNS members.

Directions
From Myrtle Beach, South Carolina go north on Highway 17 for 17 miles. At Grissittown, turn left on State Road 904, travel 1^1/$_2$ miles on 904 to Russtown Road and make a right on Russtown. Take Richardson Drive until it deadends (approx. ^{1}/$_2$ mile) into Sun Street. Take a right on Sun Street, go approximately 300 feet and the gates are on the left.

ALPINE RESORT  OHIO

P.O. Box 110
Millersburg, OH 44654

330/674-6856

FACILITIES

ACCOMMODATIONS

- Wheelchair Access
- Vacation Villas
- Cabins
- Rooms
- Cable TV
- In-room Telephone
- ■ Trailers
  - ● heated
  - ● w/bath
  - cooking
- ■ Restaurant
- Lounge
- Snack Bar
- Store

CAMPING

- ■ Tent Spaces
- ■ R/V Spaces
  - ● w/elec
  - w/water
  - w/sewer
- Disposal Station
- ■ Showers
  - ● cold
  - ● hot
- Laundromat
- Community Kitchen
- ■ Picnic Tables
- ■ Playground
- ■ Pets/Leash only

RECREATION

- Swimming Pool
- ■ Lake
- Whirlpool/Spa
- Sauna
- Exercise Equipment
- ■ Frisbee Golf
- ■ Volleyball
- Shuffleboard
- ■ Horseshoes
- Petanque
- ■ Nature Trails
- ■ Badminton
- Fishing
- ■ Recreation Hall
- Children's Activities
- Teen Activities

INFORMATION

Club Personality
Alpine Resort, open year-round for play or relaxation, and one of Ohio's most scenic camps, extends an invitation to all who are interested in the nudist lifestyle.

Description of Grounds
The resort, situated on 70 acres of well-maintained wooded land and nature trails, offers guests the opportunity to relax or to join in the many activities including lake swimming, volleyball, badminton, horseshoe, and frisbee golf.

Neighboring Sights and Attractions
There are shops, restaurants, motels, churches, and entertainment within 4 miles of the park.

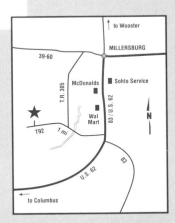

Directions
The railroad tracks are now abandoned, but there is still a hump in the road. T92 is a township gravel road, one mile from the paved road to the gate. The gate is beyond a house, not club affiliated, at the roadside.

119

CEDAR TRAILS

OHIO

11 Cow Run Road
Peebles, OH 45660

937/764-1365

FACILITIES

ACCOMMODATIONS

- ■ Wheelchair Access
  - Vacation Villas
  - Cabins
  - Rooms
  - Cable TV
  - In-room Telephone
- ■ Trailers (3)
  - ● heated (3)
  - ● w/bath (2)
  - ● cooking (3)
  - Restaurant
  - Lounge
- ■ Snack Bar
  - Store

CAMPING

- ■ Tent Spaces
- ■ R/V Spaces (2)
  - ● w/elec
    - w/water
    - w/sewer
- ■ Disposal Station
- ■ Showers
  - cold
  - ● hot (3)
- ■ Laundromat
- ■ Community Kitchen
- ■ Picnic Tables (2)
- ■ Playground
- ■ Pets/Leash only

RECREATION

- Swimming Pool
- ■ Lake (1 acre)
- ■ Whirlpool/Spa
  - Sauna
  - Exercise Equipment
  - Tennis
- ■ Volleyball
- ■ Shuffleboard
- ■ Horseshoes
- ■ Petanque
  - Miniten
- ■ Badminton
- ■ Fishing
- ■ Recreation Hall
- ■ Children's Activities
- ■ Teen Activities
- ■ Frisbee Golf

● denotes availability
■

INFORMATION

Club Personality
Nestled in the Appalachian foothills of southeastern Ohio, Cedar Trails is situated on sixty acres of rolling meadows and virgin forest designed to take guests "back to the country in style" for year-round friendship and fun.

Description of Grounds
The 60-acre campground includes a swimming lake with sand bottom and beach, a heated bathhouse, an air conditioned/heated clubhouse for year-round activities, a wood heated hot tub with whirlpool jets, game courts, hiking trails and a meditation area.

Neighboring Sights and Attractions
Ohio historical sites, including Serpent Mound, Rocky Fork Lake for boating and water skiing, Kings Island and Cincinnati Riverfront.

Honored Discounts
Discounts for AANR and Adventure Camping Network members.

Directions
Cedar Trails is easily accessible from Ohio State Route 73. Just one mile west of Serpent Mound in the town of Louden, north one mile on Elmville Road and left on first gravel road which is Cow Run Road. 0.5 mile to sign on right to entrance.

GREEN VALLEY

P.O. Box 740
Bath, OH 44210

OHIO

216/659-3812

FACILITIES

ACCOMMODATIONS

Wheelchair Access
Vacation Villas
■ Cabins (2)
Rooms
Cable TV
In-room Telephone
■ Trailers (3)
● heated
w/bath
cooking
Restaurant
Lounge
Snack Bar
■ Store

CAMPING

■ Tent Spaces (12)
■ R/V Spaces (83)
● w/elec (83)
● w/water (83)
● w/sewer (23)
■ Disposal Station
■ Showers
● cold (2)
● hot (2)
Laundromat
■ Community Kitchen
■ Picnic Tables (12)
■ Playground
■ Pets/Leash only

RECREATION

■ Swimming Pool (Olympic)
■ Lake (1 acre)
■ Whirlpool/Spa
Sauna
Exercise Equipment
■ Hiking Trails
■ Volleyball
■ Shuffleboard
■ Horseshoes
■ Basket Ball Courts
■ Miniten
■ Fishing
■ Recreation Hall
■ Adult Activities
■ Children's Activities
■ Teen Activities
■ Dances

INFORMATION

Club Personality
Green Valley, a cooperative member-owned campground in operation for 65 years, hosts year-round weekend/monthly dances, potlucks, and campfires for members and guests.

Description of Grounds
Green Valley has 47 secluded, wooded acres, with a lake, a pool, miles of hiking trails, shuffleboard and basketball courts, and playgrounds for the kids. Campsites, rental cabins and trailers are available and there are picnic areas for day guests.

Neighboring Sights and Attractions
Green Valley is located halfway between Cleveland and Akron, within a short drive of the Rock-N-Roll Hall of Fame, Sea World, NFL Hall of Fame and Cedar Point Amusement Park.

Honored Discounts
20% discount for all AANR and Naturist members.

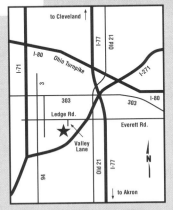

Directions
From the East: Exit I-77 at Wheatley Road (Route 176). Head west on Wheatley to Route 21. Turn left onto Route 21, and then right onto Everett Road. Head west on Everett exactly 3 miles (Everett turns into Ledge Road). Cross over State Road, top of the hill on the left.

From the West: Exit I-71 at Route 3. Head north on Route 3 until it intersects Route 94. At that intersection, bear to the right. At the stop sign, cross over Route 94. Continue east on Ledge Road, crossing over State Road as you go, top of the hill on the right.

OHIO

513/648-0401

CINCI GYMNOS

P.O. Box 40871
Cincinnati, OH 45240

 ## ACTIVITIES & RECREATION

General Information
Summers, since 1982, club members have been traveling to Ohio Valley parks, skinnydipping sites, and members' private property. During the colder months, indoor facilities are rented for club activities. Newcomers are welcome "for the natural health of the body, mind and spirit."

Hiking
Camping
Swimming
Health Spas
Recreational Workshops
Access Services

Special Events
Volleyball Picnics
Nudist History Lending Library

GREAT LAKES SUNSEEKERS

P.O. Box 405
Sylvania, OH 43560

OHIO

517/423-6296

ACTIVITIES & RECREATION

Indoor and Outdoor Sports
Hot Tubbing
House and Yard Parties
Visits to Nudist Facilities

General Information
The Great Lakes SunSeekers, a relaxed, friendly, family oriented travel club, provides year-round activities for the avid nudist, including monthly group visits to health clubs. Membership inquiries are invited and visitors are welcomed, but please contact the club in advance.

PARADISE GARDENS

OHIO

6100 Blue Rock Road
Cincinnati, OH 45247

513/385-4189

FACILITIES

ACCOMMODATIONS

- ■ Wheelchair Access
- Vacation Villas
- ■ Cabins (1)
- ■ Rooms (1)
- Cable TV
- In-room Telephone
- Trailers
  - heated
  - w/bath
  - cooking
- Restaurant
- ■ Lounge
- ■ Snack Bar
- Store

CAMPING

- ■ Tent Spaces (50)
- ■ R/V Spaces (100)
  - ● w/elec (8)
  - ● w/water (8)
  - ● w/sewer (8)
- ■ Disposal Station
- ■ Showers
  - ● cold (4)
  - ● hot (4)
- Laundromat
- Community Kitchen
- ■ Picnic Tables (6)
- ■ Playground
- ■ Pets/Leash only

RECREATION

- ■ Swimming Pool (Olympic)
- Lake
- ■ Whirlpool/Spa
- ■ Sauna
- ■ Exercise Equipment
- Tennis
- ■ Volleyball
- ■ Shuffleboard
- ■ Horseshoes
- ■ Dance/Parties
- Miniten
- ■ Badminton
- ■ Fishing
- ■ Recreation Hall
- ■ Children's Activities
- ■ Teen Activities

● ■ denotes availability

INFORMATION

Club Personality
A friendly, family oriented group of people who come in all shapes, sizes and ages. The members of Paradise Gardens are a diverse lot, representing all social, professional and economic levels.

Description of Grounds
Paradise Gardens, with its 35 acres of wooded hills and large open sunning area, comes complete with all the amenities, including an Olympic-style swimming pool, a crystal-clear lake, and a children's playground.

Neighboring Sights and Attractions
Within reasonable driving distance are King's Island, the Cincinnati Zoo, Downtown Cincinnati, Riverfront Stadium, shopping areas, motels and restaurants.

Honored Discounts
Discounts for AANR members.

Directions
Off Interstate 275, take Blue Rock Road exit. Travel northwest on Blue Rock Road. The driveway, one mile from the exit, is on the right hand side, landmarked by a red, pot-bellied stove. Visitors should call in advance.

OHIO
614/341-7037

HAVE SUN WILL TRAVEL

P.O. Box 1612
Marion, OH 43302

General Information
Have Sun Will Travel is a family oriented club whose members won MSA Family of the Year honors in 1995. The club has its own indoor pool and sauna for winter fun, and in warm weather, members visit landed clubs. The group has a youth director to ensure that the kids don't get left out of the fun.
Web Site: http://
www.midohio.net~bobsanns/nswt.html

ACTIVITIES & RECREATION

Enclosed Pool
Sauna
Winter Volleyball
Children's Activities
Travel to Landed Clubs in Summer
Diving Tank

Special Events
National Nude Weekend
Classes on Nude Recreation at OSU
Christmas Collections for the Needy

NORTHCOAST NATURISTS

P.O. Box 81601
Cleveland, OH 44181

OHIO
440/238-6177

ACTIVITIES & RECREATION

House Parties
Massage Workshops
Bowling Parties
DJ Dances
Swim Parties with "Walleyball"
Rented Facilities Include:
Raquetball
Hot Tub
Sauna
Steam Room

General Information
Northcoast Naturists is a friendly new nonlanded club growing by leaps and bounds. The club's objective is to offer a variety of nude recreation opportunities for the northern Ohio and north coast of Lake Erie area. Call, write or E-mail to receive the club's newsletter and schedule of events.
Fax: 440/243-3676
E-Mail: edb44@imperium.net

SUN MEADOW

P.O. Box 521068
Tulsa, OK 74152

OKLAHOMA

918/266-7651

FACILITIES

ACCOMMODATIONS

- Wheelchair Access
- Vacation Villas
- Cabins
- Rooms
- Cable TV
- In-room Telephone
- Trailers
  - heated
  - w/bath
  - cooking
- Restaurant
- Lounge
- Snack Bar
- Store
- Ice

CAMPING

- ■ Tent Spaces
- ■ R/V Spaces (8)
  - ● w/elec
  - ● w/water
  - w/sewer
- Disposal Station
- ■ Showers
  - ● cold (1)
  - ● hot (2)
- Laundromat
- ■ Community Kitchen
- ■ Picnic Tables
- ■ Playground
- Pets

RECREATION

- ■ Swimming Pool (16' x 32')
- Lake
- ■ Whirlpool/Spa
- ■ Sauna
- ■ Exercise Equipment
- Tennis
- ■ Volleyball
- ■ Shuffleboard
- ■ Horseshoes
- ■ Bocce Ball
- ■ Miniten
- ■ Badminton
- Fishing
- ■ Recreation Hall
- ■ Bumper Pool
- ■ Ping Pong
- ■ Activities Pavillion

■ denotes availability

INFORMATION

Club Personality
Tulsa's urban oasis for sun, fun and freedom, located a mere twenty minutes from anywhere in the city. A family-environment clothes-free recreation park for singles, couples, and families of all ages. Open March through October. Visitors and camping on weekends only.
Fax: 918/266-7550
Web Site: http://www.sunmeadow.com

Description of Grounds
Beautifully manicured rolling green lawns, with trees and shady areas. Amenities include picnic tables, hammocks in the trees, a clubhouse with fully furnished U-cook kitchen, fireplace, sauna and library. An activities pavilion provides jukebox, ping pong, bumper pool, pinball and fitness center.

Neighboring Sights and Attractions
Ten minutes from world famous Will Rogers Memorial in Claremore, and 20 minutes from all Tulsa entertainments, restaurants and arts, including Tulsa's renowned collection of Western art in the Gilcrease Museum, and the magnificent Italian villa Philbrook Art Museum.

Honored Discounts
Discounts on grounds fees for TNS, INF, FCN members.

Directions
Sun Meadow, just northeast of Tulsa, is approximately two miles northeast of the Will Rogers Turnpike gate (intersection of I-44 and U.S. 66), through Catoosa on U.S. 66. Look for the sign on the west side of the road, after passing Port City Mobile Home park on the east side of the highway.

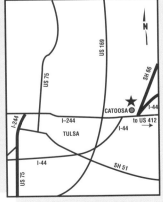

FACILITIES

ACCOMMODATIONS

- ■ Wheelchair Access
- Vacation Villas
- Cabins
- Rooms
- Cable TV
- In-room Telephone
- Trailers
  - heated
  - w/bath
  - cooking
- Restaurant
- Lounge
- Snack Bar
- Store
- ■ Ice

CAMPING

- ■ Tent Spaces (100 plus)
- ■ R/V Spaces (35)
  - ● w/elec (35)
  - ● w/water (35)
  - ● w/sewer (10)
- ■ Disposal Station
- ■ Showers
  - ● cold (6)
  - ● hot (6)
- Laundromat
- ■ Community Kitchen
- ■ Picnic Tables (10)
- ■ Playground
- ■ Pets

RECREATION

- ■ Swimming Pool (17' x 35')
- Lake
- ■ Whirlpool/Spa
- Sauna
- ■ Exercise Equipment
- Tennis
- ■ Volleyball
- ■ Shuffleboard
- ■ Horseshoes
- Petanque
- Miniten
- Badminton
- ■ Fishing
- ■ Recreation Hall
- ■ Children's Activities
- ■ Teen Activities
- ■ Picnic Pavilion

■ ● denotes availability

INFORMATION

Club Personality
Established in 1992, Oaklake Trails is a family oriented nudist park dedicated to the principle that social nudity with family and friends is wholesome, relaxing, emotionally and physically healthy, and just plain fun. Open to members year-round.

Description of Grounds
Over 400 acres of wooded, rolling hills provide the perfect setting for miles of hiking trails. A large modern clubhouse, swimming pool, hot tub, lighted volleyball court, and children's playground grace the manicured main grounds. Shady tent sites, and RV sites with water and electric hookups are conveniently located around the property.

Neighboring Sights and Attractions
Restaurants, motels, and a large shopping mall are within 15 minutes of the club. The National Cowboy Hall of Fame, Gilcrease Museum, Remington Park Racetrack, and the Tulsa and Oklahoma City Zoos are within an hour's drive.

Honored Discounts
Discounts for AANR and Naturist members. Also, group discounts, reduced weekly and monthly rates, and snowbird specials.

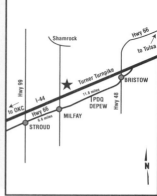

Directions
Call for current gate code before visit.
From Stroud: From the Stroud Turner Turnpike gate, go south on Highway 99 one quarter mile to Highway 66. Turn left (east) and proceed 6.6 miles to the Milfay turnoff. Turn left (north) and proceed 1.2 miles to the Oaklake Trails gate on the right (east) side of the road.
From Bristow: From the Bristow Turner Turnpike gate, go west through Bristow on Highway 66. Go 11.8 miles (3.5 miles past the PDQ store at Depew) to the Milfay turnoff. Turn right (north) and proceed 1.2 miles to the Oaklake Trails gate on the right (east) side of the road.

TUMBLEWEEDS

P.O. Box 5353
Bend, Oregon 97708

OREGON

541-383-2721

ACTIVITIES & RECREATION

Winter Swims
Potlucks
Game Nights
Canuding Trips
Travel to Clubs
Hot Tubbing

General Information
Central Oregon Tumbleweeds is a family oriented travel club. The club's location near mountains and lakes makes it a natural for such activities as skiing, fishing, hiking, and camping.
E-mail: cotweeds@aol.com

Special Events
Bed & Breakfast Retreats

OREGON

503/699-5442

HIDDEN SPRINGS

P.O. Box 17600
Portland, OR 97217

ACTIVITIES & RECREATION

Bare Bowling
Hot Tub Parties
Hot Springs Trips
Indoor Nude Recreation Nights
Travel to Landed Clubs
Travel to Nudist Conventions
Activities Planned By Members

General Information
A long established Pacific Northwest nonlanded nudist club, Hidden Springs is a cooperatively-operated family oriented club with year-round activities. Memberships are available to singles, couples and families. The club is a many-time winner as the most traveled nonlanded club in AANR. Hidden Springs publishes an informative, award winning newsletter. Membership inquiries are welcomed.

OREGON
541/488-1287

THE ROGUE SUNCATHCHERS
P.O. Box 3203
Ashland, OR 97520

General Information
The Rogue Suncatchers, a nonlanded club of about 100 members, is active year-round and is currently looking for its own land. Visitors are welcome to call and join the activity.
Fax: 541/488-4275
E-mail: miketuba@delphi.com

ACTIVITIES & RECREATION

Potlucks
Campouts
Costume and Spa Parties
Winter Swims
Adopt-A-Highway Program
Support Clothing-Optional Beach

Special Events
Annual Good-Bye-to-Summer Campout
Annual Halloween Costume Party.

SUN ROVERS
P.O. Box 3183
Portland, OR 97208

OREGON
360/892-5408

ACTIVITIES & RECREATION

Monthly Potlucks
Campouts
Participation at Landed Club Activities
Assist Beautification of Landed Clubs

General Information
Sun Rovers is a family oriented travel club with membership centered around Portland, Oregon, and southwest Washington. The 100 plus members enjoy social nudity at private homes, campouts and local landed clubs. Members lead active lifestyles and enjoy the reputation of being fun-loving participants in travel and other activities sponsored by neighboring clubs.
E-mail: sunrover@AOL.COM
Web Site: http://members.aol.com/sunrover

Special Events
Mardi Gras Dinner Dance in March
Crawdad Festival in September

RESTFUL HAVEN

P.O. Box 248
North Plains, OR 97133

OREGON

503/647-2449

FACILITIES

ACCOMMODATIONS

- ■ Wheelchair Access
- Vacation Villas
- Cabins
- Rooms
- Cable TV
- In-room Telephone
- Trailers
  - heated
  - w/bath
  - cooking
- Restaurant
- Lounge
- ■ Snack Bar (Weekends)
- ■ Boutique

CAMPING

- ■ Tent Spaces (25)
- ■ R/V Spaces (44)
  - ● w/elec (44)
  - ● w/water (44)
  - ● w/sewer(14)
- ■ Disposal Station
- ■ Showers
  - cold
  - ● hot (10)
- ■ Laundromat
- ■ Community Kitchen
- Picnic Tables
- ■ Playground
- ■ Pets/Leash only

RECREATION

- ■ Swimming Pool (40' x 60')
- Lake
- ■ Whirlpool/Spa
- ■ Sauna
- Exercise Equipment
- Tennis
- ■ Volleyball
- ■ Shuffleboard
- ■ Horseshoes
- ■ Smash Ball
- Miniten
- Badminton
- Fishing
- ■ Recreation Hall
- Children's Activities
- ■ Hiking Trails

■ ● denotes availability

INFORMATION

Club Personality
Restful Haven, a secure and secluded resort in Oregon wine country, provides hassle-free leisure on 104 acres of forested private land.
Web Site: http://www.cybernude.com/restful

Description of Grounds
A lush green lawn, miles of hiking trails, a sixty-foot heated pool, sauna, volleyball, horseshoes and shuffleboard courts provide a choice of exercise or relaxation.

Neighboring Sights and Attractions
An hour from ocean beaches, deep sea fishing, and the renowned Columbia River nude beach. Within 30 minutes of groceries, restaurants, shops, vineyard tasting rooms and golf at nationally known Pumpkin Ridge.

Honored Discounts
Discounts for AANR and Naturist members.

Directions
From Portland west on Highway 26 (Sunset Highway) about 20 miles to Exit 55—Dersham Road/Mountaindale turn right for about 2 miles to N.W. Dairy Creek Road. Turn right. Stay on this road for about 7 miles. Turn right at 27100 N.W. Dairy Creek Road into a gravel road leading to the clubhouse and office area.

SQUAW MOUNTAIN RANCH

P.O. Box 4452
Portland, OR 97208

OREGON

503/630-6136

FACILITIES

ACCOMMODATIONS

- Wheelchair Access
  Vacation Villas
- Teepee (Summer)
- Rooms (3)
  Cable TV
  In-room Telephone
- Trailers
  - heated
    w/bath
  - cooking
  Restaurant
  Lounge
  Snack Bar
- Store

CAMPING

- Tent Spaces (20 plus)
- R/V Spaces (40 plus)
  - w/elec (40)
  - w/water (40)
    w/sewer
  Disposal Station
- Showers
    cold
  - hot
  Laundromat
- Community Kitchen
- Picnic Tables (20 plus)
- Playground
- Pets/Leash only

RECREATION

  Swimming Pool
- Lake
- Whirlpool/Spa
- Sauna
  Exercise Equipment
  Tennis
- Volleyball
- Shuffleboard
- Horseshoes
  Petanque
  Miniten
- Badminton
- Fishing
  Lodge
  Children's Activities
- Miniature Golf
- Croquet

■ ● denotes availability

INFORMATION

Club Personality
This oldest landed club west of the Mississippi—established in 1933—hosts an annual music festival on the weekend before Labor Day. Guests who use the lodge must bring their own food and bedding. Open year-round, but limited in the winter months.

Description of Grounds
Located near the Mt. Hood National Forest, historic Squaw Mountain Ranch is a19-acre camp in the mountains of Clackamas County, 35 miles from Portland. Visitors should call ahead for the combination to the locked gate.

Neighboring Sights and Attractions
Scenic mountains, wildlife, streams, lakes, Bagby Hot Springs and Mount Hood Ski Resort are close by. The Willamettans and Restful Haven, neighboring clubs, are within 100 miles. Shops, restaurants, motels, churches and entertainment may be found in Estacada, 13 miles away.

Honored Discounts
Discounts for AANR and Naturist members.

Directions
Please call ahead for combination to locked gate. From Highway 205 take Highway 224, 18 miles east to Estacada. Travel through Estacada on Highway 224 to the 26 mile marker. Turn left onto Falls Creek Road, follow about one-half mile to stop sign on Divers Road, turn left to next stop sign on Squaw Mountain Road and turn right. Follow Squaw Mountain Road to nine mile marker and look for SMR mailbox. Turn right onto dirt road for one mile into the Ranch.

THE WILLAMETTANS

37000 Parsons Creek Road
Springfield, OR 97478

OREGON

541/933-2809

FACILITIES

ACCOMMODATIONS

- ■ Wheelchair Access
  Vacation Villas
  Cabins
- ■ Rooms (1)
  Cable TV
  In-room Telephone
- ■ Trailers (4)
  - ● heated
    w/bath
  - ● cooking
    Restaurant
- ■ Lounge (Summer Weekends)
- ■ Snack Bar (Summer Weekends)
- ■ Gift Shop

CAMPING

- ■ Tent Spaces (50)
- ■ R/V Spaces (50)
  - ● w/elec (35)
  - ● w/water (35)
  - ● w/sewer (6)
- ■ Disposal Station
- ■ Showers
    cold
  - ● hot (7)
- ■ Laundromat
  Community Kitchen
- ■ Picnic Tables (20)
- ■ Playground
- ■ Pets/Leash only

RECREATION

- ■ Swimming Pool (25' x 50')
  Lake
- ■ Whirlpool/Spa
- ■ Sauna
  Exercise Equipment
- ■ Tennis
- ■ Volleyball
- ■ Shuffleboard
- ■ Horseshoes
  Petanque
  Miniten
  Badminton
  Fishing
- ■ Recreation Hall
- ■ Children's Activities
- ■ Teen Activities

INFORMATION

Club Personality

The Willamettans is a long-established cooperative club with a reputation for its hospitality. The "Willies" enjoy guests and have hosted many national and regional conventions raved about by young and old alike.
Mailing Address: P.O. Box 969, Marcola, OR 97454
Web site: http://www.multinet.com/willies

Description of Grounds

The Pacific Northwest at its best. A modern, forty-acre RV Park in a secluded setting. A world of majestic fir trees in the foothills of the Cascade Mountains. Lush lawns and recreational facilities surrounded by nature trails, hiking trails and rippling creeks.

Neighboring Sights and Attractions

Less than thirty minutes from metropolitan Eugene, home of the University of Oregon. Within ninety minutes of the majestic Pacific Ocean or the High Cascades for summer and winter recreation. In the heart of Willamette Valley wine country.

Honored Discounts

Twenty percent discounts on grounds fees to members of AANR and other recognized nudist organizations.

Directions

Take Interstate 105 exit (Eugene/Springfield) east two and one-half miles to 42nd St./Jasper exit. Left to Marcola Road, right on Marcola Road nine miles to Parsons Creek Road, left 2.2 miles to mailbox #37000 AANR/NWNA. Take a left up the gravel road 0.3 miles to the gate. Office hours are 9 a.m. to 6 p.m. during summer months. Call ahead to verify overnight accommodations.

BEECHWOOD LODGE

PENNSYLVANIA

P.O. Box 145
Ashfield, PA 18212

717/386-4449

FACILITIES

ACCOMMODATIONS

Wheelchair Access
Vacation Villas
Cabins
■ Rooms
Cable TV
In-room Telephone
Trailers
  heated
  w/bath
  cooking
■ Restaurant
Lounge
■ Snack Bar
Store

CAMPING

■ Tent Spaces
■ R/V Spaces
  ● w/elec
  ● w/water
  w/sewer
Disposal Station
■ Showers
  ● cold
  ● hot
Laundromat
Community Kitchen
■ Picnic Tables
■ Playground
■ Pets/Leash only

RECREATION

■ Swimming Pool
Lake
■ Whirlpool/Spa
■ Sauna
■ Exercise Equipment
■ Tennis
■ Volleyball
Shuffleboard
Horseshoes
Petanque
Miniten
■ Badminton
Fishing
■ Recreation Hall
Children's Activities
Teen Activities

■ ● denotes availability

INFORMATION

Club Personality
Beechwood Lodge and its 15 year-round residents welcome visitors to the club's 38 acres of open, grassy areas surrounded by trees. Open year-round.

Description of Grounds
Rental rooms, numerous tent spaces, and RV sites with water and electric hookups are available. The large enclosed whirlpool is open at all times, and the oil-fired sauna is available any time two or more people wish to use it.

Neighboring Sights and Attractions
Skiing, a golf course, and the Appalachian Trail are close by. Restaurants, motels, churches, shops and entertainment are all within four miles of the park.

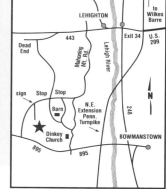

Directions
Please see map.

BROKEN ARROW

R.R.1 Box 266D
Polk, PA 16342

PENNSYLVANIA

814/432-8606

FACILITIES

ACCOMMODATIONS

Wheelchair Access
Vacation Villas
Cabins
Rooms
Cable TV
In-room Telephone
■ Trailers (1)
  ● heated
  ● w/bath
  ● cooking
Restaurant
Lounge
Snack Bar
Store

CAMPING

■ Tent Spaces (10)
■ R/V Spaces
    w/elec
    w/water
    w/sewer
  Disposal Station
■ Showers
    cold
  ● hot (1)
  Laundromat
■ Community Kitchen
■ Picnic Tables (6)
  Playground
  Pets/Leash only

RECREATION

Swimming Pool
■ Lake (2 acres)
Whirlpool/Spa
Sauna
Exercise Equipment
Tennis
■ Volleyball
Shuffleboard
■ Horseshoes
Petanque
Miniten
■ Badminton
■ Fishing
■ Recreation Hall
Children's Activities
Teen Activities

INFORMATION

Club Personality
Broken Arrow, a privately owned nudist club affiliated with AANR and ESA, is open from Memorial Day through Labor Day and beyond, weather permitting. Its peaceful surroundings, and the warm hospitality of its members, bid welcome to folks interested in the nudist lifestyle.

Description of Grounds
The club is set in 90 acres of northwestern Pennsylvania's lush forest region. There's a two-acre spring fed lake for swimming and fishing, a picnic shelter where members gather to share dinners, a fire pit for warmth on cool evenings, and picnic tables scattered throughout the grounds. Its rustic charm makes it ideal for relaxation.

Neighboring Sights and Attractions
Within a short distance of the camp are found the world's first oil region — Drake's Well, the Titusville steam railway, the Pithole Museum, and Grove City Factory outlet stores.

Honored Discounts
Discounts for AANR, The Naturist Society, and other nudist organization members.

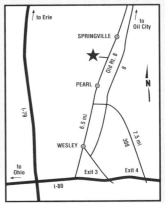

Directions
From I-80, exit #3 (Barkeyville) turn north on New Route 8, just a little over 5 miles to Route 308 exit. At the stop sign turn left (Go under New Route 8) 1/4 mile there is a Y in the road. Stay right at stop sign, turn right. One mile on the left is Broken Arrow Lane. Follow the lane to the mobile home and sound your horn.

PENNSYLVANIA

717/244-5378

HILLTOPPERS SUN CLUB

4290 List Road
Red Lion, PA 17356

ACTIVITIES & RECREATION

Tri-State Volleyball Competition
Superbowl of Volleyball Participation
Trips to Free Beaches and Nudist Facilities

General information
A full-member travel club affiliated with the American Association for Nude Recreation. Write for more information.

JUVENATION NATURISTS

P.O. Box 50
Eagleville, PA 19408

ACTIVITIES & RECREATION

Dancing
Hot Tubbing
Theme Parties
Movies
Professional Massage Therapist
Talk Circles and Introductory Games
House Parties

PENNSYLVANIA

610/631-0880

General Information
Juvenation Naturists is a travel club that meets in Royersford, near King of Prussia, Pennsylvania. The club's purpose is to help people relax and become rejuvenated through therapeutic touch, hot tubbing, and getting to know new people. The club is unique in that it is open to nudists and nonnudists alike, permitting insight into different lifestyles.
Fax: 610/631-1622
E-mail: JuvNat@aol.com

PENNSYLVANIA

215/438-6833

METRO NATURISTS

P.O. Box 165
Bensalem, PA 19020

 **ACTIVITIES & RECREATION**

General Information
A family oriented, nonlanded club serving greater Philadelphia, southern New Jersey and northern Delaware. *Metro Strip*, the club's monthly newsletter, is available to members and nudist groups. Membership inquiries are welcome.

Spa and Pool Parties
Outings to Dinner Theaters
and Dances
Vacation Trips
Visits to Landed Resorts

TIMBER TRAILS

PENNSYLVANIA

230 Old Laudermilch
Hersey, PA 17033

ACTIVITIES & RECREATION

Sunning
Swimming
Hot Tubbing
Potlucks

General Information
Timber Trails is a small, but growing, nonlanded club. Activities are held at members' homes. Continuing a nine-year tradition, the club actively supports Artists Days in the Harrisburg/York/Lancaster area. The club welcomes families and singles. Write for more information.

Special Events
Artists Days

PENN SYLVAN HEALTH SOCIETY

R.D. 3, Box 3770
Mohnton, PA 19540

PENNSYLVANIA

717/445-6330

FACILITIES

ACCOMMODATIONS

Wheelchair Access
Vacation Villas
Cabins
■ Rooms (8)
Cable TV
In-room Telephone
Trailers
   heated
   w/bath
   cooking
Restaurant
Lounge
Snack Bar
Store

CAMPING

■ Tent Spaces (20)
■ R/V Spaces (8)
   ● w/elec
   ● w/water
   w/sewer
■ Disposal Station
■ Showers
   ● cold (10)
   ● hot (10)
Laundromat
Community Kitchen
■ Picnic Tables (10)
■ Playground
■ Pets/Leash only

RECREATION

■ Swimming Pool (70' x 35')
Lake
■ Whirlpool/Spa
■ Sauna
Exercise Equipment
■ Tennis
■ Volleyball
■ Shuffleboard
Horseshoes
Petanque
Miniten
■ Badminton
Fishing
■ Recreation Hall
Children's Activities
Teen Activities

■ ● denotes availability
■

INFORMATION

Club Personality
Located 12 miles from Reading—the outlet capital of the world—this family oriented resort is just a short drive from the picturesque Amish towns of Pennsylvania's Lancaster County.

Description of Grounds
Situated on 81 acres of beautiful secluded woodland, Penn Sylvan has all of the expected amenities including a large heated swimming pool, volleyball, tennis, badminton and shuffleboard courts, ping pong tables, an indoor whirlpool, and playground facilities for the children.

Neighboring Sights and Attractions
Penn Sylvan is located in southern Berks County, just minutes from the Lancaster County line. This is the heart of Pennsylvania Dutch country, with outlet and antique shopping nearby. Close by, too, are Hershey Park and Dorney Park.

Honored Discounts
Discounts for AANR members.

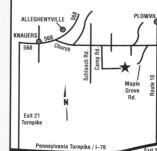

Directions
From the west: Pennsylvania Turnpike exit 21 (Lancaster-Reading) take 222 north to 568. Right on 568 to Y at Alleghenyville Church. Bear right on Alleghenyville Road to Camp Road. Two blocks left at mail boxes. From the east: Pennsylvania Turnpike exit 22 (Morgantown). Route 10 to Plowville, left on Maple Grove Road, three and one-half miles to Camp Road. Left two blocks, left at mail boxes.

136

383 State Line Road
Darlington, PA 16115

412/846-5984

FACILITIES

ACCOMMODATIONS

- Wheelchair Access
- Vacation Villas
- Cabins
- ■ Rooms (4)
- Cable TV
- In-room Telephone
- Trailers
  - heated
  - w/bath
  - cooking
- Restaurant
- Lounge
- ■ Snack Bar (Weekends)
- Store

CAMPING

- ■ Tent Spaces (100)
- ■ R/V Spaces (100)
  - ● w/elec
  - ● w/water
  - w/sewer
- ■ Disposal Station
- ■ Showers
  - cold
  - ● hot (11)
- ■ Laundromat
- Community Kitchen
- ■ Picnic Tables (30)
- ■ Playground
- Pets/Leash only

RECREATION

- ■ Heated Swimming Pool (25'x50')
- Lake
- ■ Whirlpool/Spa
- ■ Sauna
- ■ Exercise Equipment
- ■ Tennis
- ■ Volleyball
- ■ Shuffleboard
- ■ Horseshoes
- ■ Bocci Ball
- Badminton
- Fishing
- ■ Recreation Hall
- ■ Children's Activities
- ■ Teen Activities
- ■ Dances

INFORMATION

Club Personality
White Thorn Lodge is a 105-acre family campground owned and operated by its members. Visitors are welcomed from late May through mid-September. Home of the Volleyball Superbowl, the weekend after Labor Day.
Fax: 412/847-4136
Pay phone: 412/843-9916

Description of Grounds
Modern yet rustic camp in the hills and valleys of Beaver County. Miles of wooded trails surround the camping area.

Neighboring Sights and Attractions
Modern Pittsburgh, historic Fort Pitt, parks, museums, libraries and many historical sights are nearby. There is shopping in Chippewa, 8 miles away.

Honored Discounts
Discounts for AANR members.

Directions
White Thorn Lodge is located in western Pennsylvania along the Ohio line, 5 miles from Negley, Ohio, and 50 miles from downtown Pittsburgh. Mail is delivered from the Darlington post office, 9 miles away.

PENNSYLVANIA

412/823-9021

General Information
This nonlanded club was founded in 1981 as a family oriented social organization, and has a growing membership. An indoor pool in the Pittsburgh area is rented on a wintertime basis. Inquiries and visitors are welcome. Write or call for more information.

WEST PENN NATURISTS

P.O. Box 131
East McKeesport, PA 15035

ACTIVITIES & RECREATION

Winter Swimming
Volleyball
Monthly Events

DYER WOODS

114 Johnson Road
Foster, RI 02825

RHODE ISLAND

401/397-3007

ACCOMMODATIONS & RECREATION

Rental Cabins
RV Sites
Filtered Pond
Whirlpool/Spa
Sauna
Volleyball
Horseshoes
Bocce Ball
Recreation Hall
Playground

Club Personality
Dyer Woods is a private, family oriented campground in a country setting. Its facilities and equipment came into being through the combined efforts of its members. Evening Reservations/Emergency: 401/392-3064

Description of Grounds
The camp is located on an old 200-acre farm with meadows, woodlands, clearings, roads and paths. A true country setting, with the hills and valleys typical of western Rhode Island. Dyer Woods is a simple outdoor-type club, with 50 permanently-leased campsites hooked up to water and electricity.

Neighboring Sights and Attractions
Close to Newport, Foxwood Resort and Casino, Sturbridge Village, Historical Providence, Roger Williams Park and Zoo, Cape Cod, Mystic Seaport Village and Aquarium. Close to some beautiful beaches, too, and one mile from the Foster Country Club golf course.